Using Accounting Software

Software

Workbook

Tara Askham

Published by Osborne Books Limited
Tel 01905 748071
Email books@osbornebooks.co.uk
Website www.osbornebooks.co.uk

Design by Laura Ingham

Printed by CPI Group (UK) Limited, Croydon, CR0 4YY, on environmentally friendly, acid-free paper from managed forests.

British Library Cataloguing in Publication Data
A catalogue record for this book is available from the British Library

ISBN 978 1909173 743

Contents

Introduction

Practice assessments

Answers to practice assessments

Introduction

Qualifications covered

This book has been written specifically to cover the Unit 'Using Accounting Software' which is mandatory for the following qualifications:

- AAT Foundation Certificate in Accounting – Level 2
- AAT Foundation Diploma in Accounting and Business – Level 2
- AAT Foundation Award in Accounting Software – Level 2
- AAT Foundation Certificate in Accounting at SCQF Level 5

This book provides four full Practice Assessments to prepare the student for the Computer Based Assessments. They are based directly on the structure, style and content of the sample assessment material provided by the AAT at www.aat.org.uk. Suggested answers to the Practice Assessments are set out in this book.

The Sage system (Version 22) has been chosen as it is widely used both by businesses and by training providers.

Osborne Study and Revision Materials

The materials featured on the previous page are tailored to the needs of students studying this unit and revising for the assessment. They include:

- **Tutorials:** paperback books with practice activities
- **Student Zone:** access to Osborne Books online resources
- **Osborne Books App:** Osborne Books ebooks for mobiles and tablets

Visit www.osbornebooks.co.uk for details of study and revision resources and access to online material.

Practice
assessment 1
Frances Fireplaces

Instructions to candidates

This assessment asks you to input data into a computerised accounting package and produce documents and reports. There are 13 tasks and it is important that you attempt all tasks.

The time allowed to complete this computerised accounting assessment is **2 hours, plus 15 minutes reading time**.

Additional time up to a maximum of 1 hour may be scheduled by your tutor to allow for delays due to computer issues such as printer queues.

It is important that you print **all** reports and documents specified in the tasks so your work can be assessed. A checklist has been provided at the end of the assessment to help you check that all documents and reports have been printed.

If your computerised accounting system allows for the generation of PDFs, these can be generated instead of hard copy prints. Screenshots saved as image files are also acceptable.

Data

Frances Fireplaces is an existing business that supplies bespoke fireplaces to the local area. The owner is **Frances Webster,** who operates as a sole trader.

The business has previously kept manual books but from **1 Oct 20-X**, the accounts are to be computerised.

You are employed as an Accounts Assistant.

You can assume that all documentation has been checked for accuracy and authorised by Frances Webster.

Cash and credit sales are analysed in **two** ways:

- Gas fires

- Electric fires

Some nominal ledger accounts have already been allocated account codes. You may need to amend account names or create other account codes.

The business is registered for VAT (Standard Accounting). The rate of VAT charged on all goods and services sold by Frances Fireplaces is 20%.

All expenditure should be analysed as you feel appropriate.

Before you start you should:

- Set the financial year to start on **1 October of the current year**.

- Set the software date as **31 October of the current year**.

- Set up the company details by entering the name **Frances Fireplaces** and the address: **24 Steinbeck Street, Firtown, East Beeston, FW6 3RB**. In a training environment you should add your name after the business name to identify your printouts.

- The VAT number is 578 3645 63 and the standard rate VAT of 20% is charged on all sales.

Task 1

(a)   Set up customer records for each of the customers below, with opening balances as at 1 October 20-X.

(b)   Generate a customer activity report on screen. Check it for accuracy and, if necessary, correct any errors. You do not need to print the customer activity report.

Customer name and address	Contact name and number	Customer account code	Opening balance as at 1 October 20-X	Payment terms	Credit limit
Cranthorne Interiors 124 Cranthorne Street Gilford GC26 1TU	Habibe Mahmood 0162 748542	CRA001	£4,304.40	30 days	£5,000.00
Homeware Showroom 23A Stone Street Gilford GC22 7BY	Claire Hemmingway 0162 147526	HOM001	£650.50	30 days	£25,000.00
Shirley Styles Unit 24 Teabrook Industrial Estate Beeston BE4 9AL	Phillip Sandford 0178 264240	SHI001	£1,670.00	30 days	£28,000.00

Task 2

(a) Set up supplier records for each of the suppliers below, with opening balances as at 1 October 20-X.

(b) Generate a supplier activity report on screen. Check it for accuracy and, if necessary, correct any errors. You do not need to print the supplier activity report.

Supplier name and address	Contact name and number	Supplier account code	Opening balance as at 1 October 20-X	Payment terms	Credit limit
Chris Carrington Ltd 9A Gedling Lane Beeston BC4 6PY	Mark Carrington 0178 364214	CHR001	£980.00	30 days	£2,500.00
East Town Electrics 198 Grange Avenue Wilford WS7 2CS	Seema Tomlinson 0191 471256	EAS001	£2,876.50	30 days	£8,000.00
Mark Sharpe 64 Milford Rise Gilford GC14 8LA	Mark Sharpe 0162 589301	MAR001	£940.55	30 days	£3,500.00

Task 3

(a) Using the list of nominal ledger balances below, set up nominal ledger records for each account. Select, amend or create nominal ledger codes where required.

(b) Generate a trial balance on screen. Check it for accuracy and, if necessary, correct any errors. You do not need to print the trial balance.

Opening Trial Balance as at 1 October 20-X

Account name	Note	Debit £	Credit £
Bank		16,000.00	
Petty cash		160.00	
Office equipment – cost		15,400.00	
Office equipment – accumulated depreciation			3,080.00
Motor vehicles – cost		32,360.00	
Motor vehicles – accumulated depreciation			8,090.00
Sales ledger control account	1	6,624.90	
Purchase ledger control account	1		4,797.05
VAT on sales	2		7,420.60
VAT on purchases	2	3,930.00	
Capital			31,087.25
Bank loan			20,000.00
Rent income	3		NIL
Sales – Gas fires	3		NIL
Sales – Electric fires	3		NIL
Drawings	3		NIL
Goods for resale	3	NIL	
Bank deposit	3	NIL	
Gross wages	3	NIL	
General rates	3	NIL	
Vehicle insurance	3	NIL	
Postage	3	NIL	
Office stationery	3	NIL	
Repairs and renewals	3	NIL	
Bank charges	3	NIL	
Totals		**74,474.90**	**74,474.90**

Notes:

1   As you have already entered opening balances for customers and suppliers you may not need to enter these balances, you will need to check whether your accounting software requires you to make a separate adjustment.

2   The accounting software you are using may not require you to post these balances individually. The opening balance on the account is £3,490.60 (credit) if posting as a single brought forward balance.

3   These nominal accounts are needed for transactions taking place in October 20-X.

In the rest of the assessment, you will only make entries to the nominal ledger accounts you created in Task 3. You will not be required to make entries to any accounts other than those you have already created.

Task 4

Using the information from the sales day book and sales returns day book below, enter these transactions into the computer.

Summary of sales invoices

Date 20-X	Customer	Invoice number	Gross	VAT	Net	Gas fires	Electric fires
2 October	Shirley Styles	280	16,648.80	2,774.80	13,874.00	13,874.00	
10 October	Homeware Showroom	281	21,009.60	3,501.60	17,508.00	12,908.00	4,600.00
	Totals		37,658.40	6,276.40	31,382.00	26,782.00	4,600.00

Summary of sales credit notes

Date 20-X	Customer	Credit note number	Gross	VAT	Net	Gas fires	Electric fires
12 October	Cranthorne Interiors	67	84.00	14.00	70.00		70.00
14 October	Shirley Styles	68	1,944.00	324.00	1,620.00	1,620.00	
	Totals		2,028.00	338.00	1,690.00	1,620.00	70.00

Task 5

Enter the following purchase invoices and purchase credit note into the computer.

Purchase Invoice

```
┌─────────────────────────────────────────────────────────────────────┐
│  ━━━━━━━━━━━━━━━━━━━━━━━━━ INVOICE ━━━━━━━━━━━━━━━━━━━━━        │
│                      East Town Electrics                             │
│               198 Grange Avenue, Wilford, WS7 2CS                    │
│               VAT registration number 748 5462 35                    │
│                                                                       │
│   FAO Frances Webster            invoice no      745226             │
│   Frances Fireplaces                                                 │
│   24 Steinbeck Street            date        13 October 20-X        │
│   Firtown                                                            │
│   East Beeston                                                       │
│   FW6 3RB                                                            │
│                                                                       │
│   Supply of goods for resale                            £3,740.00   │
│                                                                       │
│                                   goods total           £3,740.00   │
│                                                                       │
│                                   VAT @ 20%              £748.00     │
│                                                                       │
│                                   TOTAL                 £4,488.00   │
└─────────────────────────────────────────────────────────────────────┘
```

Purchase Credit note

```
┌─────────────────────────────────────────────────────────────────────┐
│  ━━━━━━━━━━━━━━━━━━━━━ CREDIT NOTE ━━━━━━━━━━━━━━━━━━━━       │
│                      East Town Electrics                             │
│               198 Grange Avenue, Wilford, WS7 2CS                    │
│               VAT registration number 748 5462 35                    │
│                                                                       │
│   Frances Fireplaces             credit note no   CN541            │
│   24 Steinbeck Street                                                │
│   Firtown                        date        17 October 20-X        │
│   East Beeston                                                       │
│   FW6 3RB                                                            │
│                                                                       │
│   Goods for resale returned                              £47.00     │
│                                                                       │
│                                   goods total            £47.00     │
│                                                                       │
│                                   VAT @ 20%              £9.40       │
│                                                                       │
│                                   TOTAL                  £56.40     │
└─────────────────────────────────────────────────────────────────────┘
```

Purchase Invoice

INVOICE

Chris Carrington Limited
9A Gedling Lane, Beeston, BC4 6PY
VAT registration number 851 6874 74

invoice to

Frances Fireplaces	
24 Steinbeck Street	
Firtown	
East Beeston	
FW6 3RB	

invoice no   **0014582**

date   **25 October 20-X**

Repairs to the showroom	£876.00
VAT @ 20%	£175.20
Total invoice	£1,051.20

Task 6

(a)   You have received the following email. Enter this transaction into the computer.

Email	
To:	Accounts Assistant
From:	Frances Webster
Date:	16 October 20-X
Subject:	Vehicle Insurance

Hello

Today I have renewed the vehicle insurance on two of our company vehicles. The amount totalled £1,490.60 and I have paid it using the business debit card.

Please record this transaction. VAT is not applicable.

Kind regards

Frances

(b)   You have received the following email. Enter this transaction into the computer.

Email	
To:	Accounts Assistant
From:	Frances Webster
Date:	17 October 20-X
Subject:	Transfer between bank accounts

Hello

Today I have completed an online transfer to transfer £10,000 from the bank current account into the bank deposit account.

Please record this transaction. VAT is not applicable.

Kind regards

Frances

(c)   Enter the following cash sales receipts into the computer.

Frances Fireplaces	Receipt No: 56
	date 29 October 20-X

description	amount	
	£	p
X2 Gas fires	434	40
Total (Including VAT @ 20%)	434	40

VAT reg no. 578 3645 63

Frances Fireplaces	Receipt No: 57
	date 29 October 20-X

description	amount	
	£	p
X4 Gas fires	724	00
X1 Electric fires	146	00
	870	00
VAT @ 20%	174	00
Total	1,044	00

VAT reg no. 578 3645 63

Task 7

Enter the following customer receipts from the documents below.

BACS REMITTANCE ADVICE

TO

Frances Fireplaces
24 Steinbeck Street
Firtown
East Beeston
FW6 3RB

FROM

Shirley Styles
Unit 24
Teabrook Industrial Estate
Beeston
BE4 9AL

Date 26 October 20-X

Your ref	Our ref		Amount
O/bal	INV2366		£1,670.00
		Total	**£1,670.00**

THIS HAS BEEN PAID BY BACS CREDIT TRANSFER DIRECTLY TO YOUR BANK ACCOUNT

Gilford Bank plc
285 High Street
Gilford, GJ7 5RD

Date   26 October 20-X

Frances Fireplaces

Four thousand, two hundred and twenty

pounds and forty pence

£ 4,220.40

A/c payee only

Habibe Mahmood

203654   47858765   10-24-89   Cranthorne Interiors

NB: This cheque pays the balance as at 1 October less credit note 67

Newford Bank
36 High Street
East Beeston, BE6 8RN

Date   28 October 20-X

Frances Fireplaces

Two thousand pounds only

£ 2,000.00

A/c payee only

Claire Hemmingway

632012   78426598   26-04-62   Homeware Showroom

NB: This cheque is a payment on account

Task 8

(a)   Enter the following payments to suppliers into the computer.

Payments to suppliers

Date (20-X)	Supplier	Type	£	Details
20 October	East Town Electrics	Cheque 020142	2,820.10	Pays balance as at 1 October less credit note CN541
24 October	Mark Sharpe	BACS	940.55	Pays balance as at 1 October

Task 9

Refer to the standing order schedule below.

(a)   Set up recurring entries for the transactions below.

(b)   Print a screenshot of the screen setting up each of the recurring entries. Save these as Evidence 5a and Evidence 5b.

(c)   Process the first payment for each standing order.

Details	Amount	Frequency	Total number of payments	Payment start date 20-X
STO receipt for rental income from S Shaw	£600.00 plus VAT	Monthly	6	1 October
STO payment for rates to Gilford Council	£142.00 (VAT Exempt)	Monthly	12	5 October

Task 10

(a)   A petty cash reimbursement request has been received for £40.00 to restore the petty cash account to £200.00. Enter a transfer from the bank account to the petty cash account for this amount using cheque number 020141 dated 1 October 20-X.

(b)   Enter the following petty cash vouchers into the computer.

petty cash voucher		Number *101*
	date	*17 Oct 20-X*

description	amount	
	£	p
Postage stamps (VAT not applicable)	*8*	*60*
	8	*60*
Receipt attached		

petty cash voucher		Number *102*
	date	*18 Oct 20-X*

description	amount	
	£	p
Envelopes	*12*	*00*
VAT	*2*	*40*
Total	*14*	*40*
Receipt attached		

petty cash voucher		Number *103*
	date	*18 Oct 20-X*

description	amount	
	£	p
Ink for printer (VAT included)	*16*	*50*
	16	*50*
Receipt attached		

Task 11

Enter the following journals into the computer.

Journal entry 061 30 October 20-X	Dr	Cr
Wages	1,000.00	
Drawings		1,000.00
Correction of posting error. Wages incorrectly posted to drawings.		

Journal entry 062 30 October 20-X	Dr	Cr
Bank	18.00	
General rates		18.00
An error in the amount shown on the standing order schedule for general rates.		

Task 12

Refer to the following bank statement.

(a) Enter the bank charges (no VAT) which have not yet been accounted for.

(b) Reconcile the bank statement and save a screenshot of the bank reconciliation screen showing reconciled items. Save this as Evidence 6. If the bank statement does not reconcile, check your work and make the necessary corrections.

GILFORD BANK PLC

Statement of account

Gilford Bank plc
285 High Street
Gilford
GJ7 5RD

Account
Frances Fireplaces
24 Steinbeck Street
Firtown
East Beeston
FW6 3RB

Date: 31 October 20-X

Date	Details	Debit £	Credit £	Balance £	
01-Oct	Opening balance			16,000.00	C
01-Oct	STO Rent S Shaw		720.00	16,720.00	C
05-Oct	STO Gilford Council	124.00		16,596.00	C
05-Oct	020141	40.00		16,556.00	C
17-Oct	Transfer from 102745874	10,000.00		6,556.00	C
18-Oct	Debit card	1,490.60		5,065.40	C
26-Oct	BACS Shirley Styles		1,670.00	6,735.40	C
26-Oct	Credit 203475		4,220.40	10,955.80	C
27-Oct	020142	2,820.10		8,135.70	C
27-Oct	BACS Mark Sharpe	940.55		7,195.15	C
30-Oct	Bank charges	23.60		7,171.55	C
	D = Debit C = Credit				

Task 13

Documentation of evidence

You are now required to generate the following documents to demonstrate your competence:

Document and reports	Save/print as:
A document showing all transactions with each customer during October 20-X	**Evidence 1a – Name – AAT number**
A document showing the balance owed by each customer as at 31 October 20-X	**Evidence 1b – Name – AAT number**
The following information must be evidenced within these documents: • *Customer name* • *Account code* • *Payment terms*	*Depending on your software, you may need to save/print one or more documents*
A document showing all transactions with each supplier during October 20-X	**Evidence 2a – Name – AAT number**
A document showing the balance owed by each supplier as at 31 October 20-X	**Evidence 2b – Name – AAT number**
The following information must be evidenced within these documents: • *Supplier name* • *Account code* • *Payment terms*	*Depending on your software, you may need to save/print one or more documents*
An audit trail, showing full details of all transactions, including details of receipts/payments allocated to items in customer/supplier accounts and details of items in the bank account that have been reconciled	**Evidence 3 – Name – AAT number**
Trial balance as at 31 October 20-X	**Evidence 4 – Name – AAT number**
Screenshot of the recurring entry set up screen, including all relevant input detail for both entries	**Evidence 5a – Name – AAT number** **Evidence 5b – Name – AAT number**
Screenshot of the bank reconciliation screen showing reconciled items	**Evidence 6 – Name – AAT number**

Note that the accounting package you are using may not use exactly the same report names as those shown above.

Before you finish your work use the checklist below to make sure you have printed all documents and reports as specified in the assessment.

Checklist

Documents and reports	Task	X when printed
Screenshot of the recurring entry set up screen, including all relevant input detail for both recurring entries	13	
Screenshot of the bank reconciliation screen showing reconciled items	13	
A document showing all transactions with each customer during October 20-X	13	
A document showing the balance owed by each customer as at 31 October 20-X	13	
A document showing all transactions with each supplier during October 20-X	13	
A document showing the balance owed by each supplier as at 31 October 20-X	13	
An audit trail, showing full details of all transactions, including details of receipts/payments allocated to items in customer/supplier accounts and details of items in the bank account that have been reconciled	13	
Trial balance as at 31 October 20-X	13	

Practice
assessment 2
Dolby Decorating

Instructions to candidates

This assessment asks you to input data into a computerised accounting package and produce documents and reports. There are 13 tasks and it is important that you attempt all tasks.

The time allowed to complete this computerised accounting assessment is **2 hours, plus 15 minutes reading time**.

Additional time up to a maximum of 1 hour may be scheduled by your tutor to allow for delays due to computer issues such as printer queues.

It is important that you print **all** reports and documents specified in the tasks so your work can be assessed. A checklist has been provided at the end of the assessment to help you check that all documents and reports have been printed.

If your computerised accounting system allows for the generation of PDFs, these can be generated instead of hard copy prints. Screenshots saved as image files are also acceptable.

Data

Dolby Decorating has been trading for one year. They have a team of three staff to offer decorating services within the local area and also sell a range of decorating supplies. The owner is **Derek Dolby** who operates as a sole trader.

The business has previously kept manual books but from **1 March 20-X**, the accounts are to be computerised.

You are employed as a bookkeeper.

You can assume that all documentation has been checked for accuracy and authorised by Derek Dolby.

Cash and credit sales are analysed in **two** ways:

*   Decorating services

*   Decorating supplies

Some nominal ledger accounts have already been allocated account codes. You may need to amend account names or create other account codes.

The business is registered for VAT (Standard Accounting). The rate of VAT charged on all goods and services sold by Dolby Decorating is 20%.

All expenditure should be analysed as you feel appropriate.

Before you start you should:

*   Set the financial year to start on **1 March of the current year**.

*   Set the software date as **31 March of the current year**.

*   Set up the company details by entering the name **Dolby Decorating** and the address: **610 Wheatley Street, Moorhall, East Arnold, EF1 5KM**. In a training environment you should add your name after the business name to identify your printouts.

*   The VAT number is 653 4510 06 and the standard rate VAT of 20% is charged on all sales.

Task 1

(a)   From the customer record cards below, enter the information to set up customer records.

Company name: Bingham Housing	**Customer Account Code:** BIN001
Address: Unit 4 Newstead Industrial Estate Newstead Road West Arnold WF5 7HF	**Payment terms:** 30 days **Credit limit:** £23,500.00
Contact name: Sanjay Sarma **Telephone:** 0196 745240	**Email:** info@binghamhousing.co.uk **Website:** www.binghamhousing.co.uk

Company name: Limegate Decorating Stores	**Customer Account Code:** LIM001
Address: 74 Curzon Street Arnold AF8 2FW	**Payment terms:** 30 days **Credit limit:** £4,000.00
Contact name: Hannah McPhilbin **Telephone:** 0180 360214	**Email:** hannah@limegate.co.uk **Website:** www.limegate.co.uk

Company name: Town View Property Services	**Customer Account Code:** TOW001
Address: 157a Southgate Road Arnold AF5 7NV	**Payment terms:** 30 days **Credit limit:** £26,000.00
Contact name: Mary Przada **Telephone:** 0180 240240	**Email:** accounts@townviewproperties.co.uk **Website:** www.townviewproperties.co.uk

(b)   Enter the following opening balances into the customer records as at 1 March 20-X:

Bingham Housing £12,404.40

Limegate Decorating Stores £1,605.95

Town View Property Services £3,480.00

(c)   Generate a customer activity report on screen. Check it for accuracy and, if necessary, correct any errors. You do not need to print the customer activity report.

Task 2

(a)   From the supplier record cards below, enter the information to set up supplier records.

Company name: Arnold Decorating Warehouse Ltd   **Supplier Account Code:** ARN001

Address: 417 Magdala Road Louth LE6 8AN	**Payment terms:** 30 days **Credit limit:** £3,000.00
Contact name: Hollie Simpson **Telephone:** 0131 667778	**Email:** h.simpson@arnold_decorating.co.uk **Website:** www.arnolddecoratingwarehouse.co.uk

---

Company name: Campbell & Son Wholesale Ltd   **Supplier Account Code:** CAM001

Address: Unit 7 317 Manvers Road Arnold AH6 8BF	**Payment terms:** 30 days **Credit limit:** £10,000.00
Contact name: John Campbell **Telephone:** 0180 200300	**Email:** accounts@campbell.com **Website:** www.candswholesale.com

---

Company name: Walker Wallpaper Supplies   **Supplier Account Code:** WAL001

Address: 680 Davies Road Brimfield BC2 3DR	**Payment terms:** 30 days **Credit limit:** £10,000.00
Contact name: Matt Walker **Telephone:** 0117 672954	**Email:** m.walker@walkerwallpapersupplies.co.uk **Website:** www.walkerwallpapersupplies.co.uk

---

(b)   Enter the following opening balances into the supplier records as at 1 March 20-X:

Arnold Decorating Warehouse Ltd £976.20

Campbell & Son Wholesale Ltd £4,900.50

Walker Wallpaper Supplies £7,500.60

(c)   Generate a supplier activity report on screen. Check it for accuracy and, if necessary, correct any errors. You do not need to print the supplier activity report.

Task 3

(a) Using the list of nominal ledger balances below, set up nominal ledger records for each account. Select, amend or create nominal ledger codes where required.

(b) Generate a trial balance on screen. Check it for accuracy and, if necessary, correct any errors. You do not need to print the trial balance.

Opening Trial Balance as at 1 March 20-X

Account name	Note	Debit £	Credit £
Bank			3,460.00
Petty cash		200.00	
Plant and machinery – cost		25,600.00	
Plant and machinery – accumulated depreciation			12,800.00
Furniture		32,802.00	
Furniture – accumulated depreciation			9840.60
Motor vehicles – cost		26,882.08	
Motor vehicles – accumulated depreciation			10,752.83
Sales ledger control account	1	17,490.35	
Purchase ledger control account	1		13,377.30
VAT on sales	2		9,800.00
VAT on purchases	2	5,607.00	
Capital			48,550.70
Sales – Decorating services	3		NIL
Sales – Decorating supplies	3		NIL
Drawings	3	NIL	
Materials purchased (Wallpaper)	3	NIL	
Materials purchased (Decorating supplies)	3	NIL	
Telephone	3	NIL	
Wages	3	NIL	
Travel and subsistence	3	NIL	
General Rates	3	NIL	
Postage and Carriage	3	NIL	
Office Stationery	3	NIL	
Equipment Leasing	3	NIL	
Cleaning	3	NIL	
Bank Charges	3	NIL	
Totals		**108,581.43**	**108,581.43**

Notes:

1   As you have already entered opening balances for customers and suppliers you may not need to enter these balances, you will need to check whether your accounting software requires you to make a separate adjustment.

2   The accounting software you are using may not require you to post these balances individually. The opening balance on the account is £4,193.00 (credit) if posting as a single brought forward balance.

3   These nominal accounts are needed for transactions taking place in March 20-X.

In the rest of the assessment, you will only make entries to the nominal ledger accounts you created in Task 3. You will not be required to make entries to any accounts other than those you have already created.

Task 4

Enter the following sales invoices and sales credit notes into the computer.

Sales Invoice

INVOICE

Dolby Decorating
610 Wheatley Street, Moorhall, East Arnold, EF1 5KM

FAO: Mary Przada
Town View Property Services
157a Southgate Road
Arnold
AF5 7NV

invoice no   **TOW001/IN3010**

date   **3 March 20-X**

Decorating services	£15,780.00
Decorating supplies	£2,010.00
total	**£17,790.00**
VAT @ 20%	**£3,558.00**
Total invoice	**£21,348.00**

VAT registration number 653 4510 06

Sales Invoice

INVOICE

𝕯olby 𝕯ecorating

610 Wheatley Street, Moorhall, East Arnold, EF1 5KM

FAO: Hannah McPhilbin **Limegate Decorating Stores** **74 Curzon Street** **Arnold** **AF8 2FW**	invoice no **LIM001/IN3011** date **4 March 20-X**

Decorating services		£800.00
Decorating supplies		£607.00
	total	**£1,407.00**
	VAT @ 20%	**£281.40**
	Total invoice	**£1,688.40**

VAT registration number 653 4510 06

Sales Invoice

INVOICE

𝕯olby 𝕯ecorating

610 Wheatley Street, Moorhall, East Arnold, EF1 5KM

FAO: Sanjay Sarma **Bingham Housing** **Unit 4** **Newstead Industrial Estate** **Newstead Road** **West Arnold, WF5 7HF**	invoice no **BIN001/IN3012** date **20 March 20-X**

Decorating services		£7,093.10
	total	**£7,093.10**
	VAT @ 20%	**£1,418.62**
	Total invoice	**£8,511.72**

VAT registration number 653 4510 06

Sales Credit Note

— CREDIT NOTE —

Dolby Decorating

610 Wheatley Street, Moorhall, East Arnold, EF1 5KM

FAO: Hannah McPhilbin **Limegate Decorating Stores** **74 Curzon Street** **Arnold** **AF8 2FW**	credit note no **LIM001/C125** date **5 March 20-X**

Decorating supplies returned		£81.00
	total	**£81.00**
	VAT @ 20%	**£16.20**
	TOTAL	**£97.20**

VAT registration number 653 4510 06

Sales Credit Note

— CREDIT NOTE —

Dolby Decorating

610 Wheatley Street, Moorhall, East Arnold, EF1 5KM

FAO: Mary Przada **Town View Property Services** **157a Southgate Road** **Arnold** **AF5 7NV**	credit note no **TOW001/C126** date **23 March 20-X**

Decorating supplies returned		£4,000.00
	total	**£4,000.00**
	VAT @ 20%	**£800.00**
	TOTAL	**£4,800.00**

VAT registration number 653 4510 06

Task 5

Using the information from the purchases day book and purchase returns day book below, enter these transactions into the computer.

Date 20-X	Supplier	Invoice number	Gross	VAT	Net	Wallpaper	Decorating Supplies
02-Mar	Walker Wallpaper Supplies	INV 2978	1,872.00	312	1,560.00	1,250.00	310.00
05-Mar	Campbell & Son Wholesale Ltd	D03024	3,914.21	652.37	3,261.84	2,620.84	641.00
07-Mar	Arnold Decorating Warehouse Ltd	PI 419	1,290.96	215.16	1,075.80	1,021.00	54.80
	Totals		7,077.17	1,179.53	5,897.64	4,891.84	1,005.80

Date 20-X	Supplier	Credit note number	Gross	VAT	Net	Wallpaper	Decorating Supplies
14-Mar	Walker Wallpaper Supplies	CN622	134.78	22.46	112.32	20.00	92.32
18-Mar	Arnold Decorating Warehouse Ltd	87	38.02	6.34	31.68	31.68	0.00
	Totals		172.80	28.80	144.00	51.68	92.32

Task 6

(a)   You have received the following email. Enter this transaction into the computer.

Email
To: Bookkeeper
From: Derek Dolby
Date: 21 March 20-X
Subject: Drawings
Hello
Today I have withdrawn £175 cash out of the business bank account for personal use.
Please record this transaction. VAT is not applicable.
Kind regards
Derek

(b)   You have received the following email. Enter this transaction into the computer.

Email
To: Bookkeeper
From: Derek Dolby
Date: 30 March 20-X
Subject: Wages March 20-X
Hello
Today I sent the monthly wages payments of £4,980.00 by BACS.
Please record this transaction. VAT is not applicable.
Kind regards
Derek

(c) A cheque has been received for the goods sold below. Enter the cash sales receipt into the computer.

Cash sales receipt

Dolby Decorating		Receipt No: 87		
		date 13 March 20-X		
description			amount	
			£	p
Decorating supplies			519	00
Total (Including VAT @ 20%)			519	00

Dolby Decorating, 610 Wheatley Street, Moorhall, East Arnold, EF1 5KM
VAT reg no. 653 4510 06

Task 7

Enter the following customer receipts from the documents below.

BACS REMITTANCE ADVICE

TO
Dolby Decorating
610 Wheatley Street
Moorhall
East Arnold
EF1 5KM

FROM
Bingham Housing
Unit 4, Newstead Industrial Estate
Newstead Road
West Arnold
WF5 7HF

Date 2 March 20-X

Your ref	Our ref		Amount
O/bal	PO3647		£12,404.40
		Total	**£12,404.40**

THIS HAS BEEN PAID BY BACS CREDIT TRANSFER DIRECTLY TO YOUR BANK ACCOUNT

BACS REMITTANCE ADVICE

TO
Dolby Decorating
610 Wheatley Street
Moorhall
East Arnold
EF1 5KM

FROM
Limegate Decorating Stores
74 Curzon Street
Arnold
AF8 2FW

Date 10 March 20-X

Your ref	Our ref		Amount
LIM001/IN3011	PO10345		£1,688.40
LIM001/C125	PO10247		£97.20
		Total	**£1,591.20**

THIS HAS BEEN PAID BY BACS CREDIT TRANSFER DIRECTLY TO YOUR BANK ACCOUNT

BACS REMITTANCE ADVICE

TO
Dolby Decorating
610 Wheatley Street
Moorhall
East Arnold
EF1 5KM

FROM
Limegate Decorating Stores
74 Curzon Street
Arnold
AF8 2FW

Date 24 March 20-X

Your ref	Our ref		Amount
O/bal	PO10098		£1,605.95
		Total	**£1,605.95**

THIS HAS BEEN PAID BY BACS CREDIT TRANSFER DIRECTLY TO YOUR BANK ACCOUNT

Wenlock Building Society
68 Clifton Road
Arnold, AF6 2BE

Date *27 March 20-X*

NB: This cheque is a payment on account

Dolby Decorating

Five thousand pounds only

A/c payee only

£ *5,000.00*

M Przada

210114   12361708   20-60-50   Town View Property Services

Task 8

Enter the following payments to suppliers into the computer.

Payments to suppliers

Date (20-X)	Supplier	Type	£	Details
20 March	Arnold Decorating Warehouse Ltd	Cheque 020784	1,500.00	Payment on account
22 March	Walker Wallpaper Supplies	BACS	1,737.22	Pays invoice INV2978 less credit note CN622
23 March	Campbell & Son Wholesale Ltd	Cheque 020785	4,900.50	Pays opening balance

Task 9

Refer to the standing order/direct debit schedule below.

(a)   Set up a recurring entry for each of the transactions below.

(b)   Print a screenshot of the screen setting up each of the recurring entries. Save these as Evidence 5a and Evidence 5b.

(c)   Process the first payment for each standing order/direct debit.

Details	Amount	Frequency	Total number of payments	Payment start date 20-X
TO: TK Telephones DD payments for telephone bill	£84.00 plus VAT	Monthly	6	18 March
TO: Moorhall Rentals STO payments for photocopier rental payments (Equipment Leasing)	£106.00 plus VAT	Quarterly	4	20 March

Task 10

(a) A petty cash reimbursement request has been received for £50.00 to restore the petty cash account to £250.00. Enter a transfer from the bank account to the petty cash account for this amount using cheque number 020783 dated 1 March 20-X.

(b) Enter the following petty cash vouchers into the computer.

petty cash voucher		Number *184*	
		date *3 March 20-X*	
description		amount	
		£	p
X4 boxes of pens (VAT included)		*5*	*60*
		5	*60*
Receipt attached			

petty cash voucher		Number *185*	
		date *9 March 20-X*	
description		amount	
		£	p
Cleaning materials		*6*	*20*
VAT		*1*	*24*
Total		*7*	*44*
Receipt attached			

petty cash voucher		Number *186*	
		date *15 March 20-X*	
description		amount	
		£	p
Postage for a parcel (no VAT)		*7*	*50*
		7	*50*
Receipt attached			

```
┌─────────────────────────────────────────────────────────┐
│  petty cash voucher              Number  187            │
│                         date   23 March 20-X            │
│  ─────────────────────────────────────────────────────  │
│  description                            amount          │
│  ─────────────────────────────────────────────────────  │
│                                    │  £  │  p  │        │
│  Postage stamps (no VAT)           │  21 │ 00  │        │
│                                    ├─────┼─────┤        │
│                                    │  21 │ 00  │        │
│  Receipt attached                  │     │     │        │
│                                    │     │     │        │
└─────────────────────────────────────────────────────────┘
```

Task 11

Enter the following journal into the computer.

Journal entry 006 30 March 20-X	Dr	Cr
Sales – Decorating supplies	46.00	
Sales – Decorating services		46.00
Correction of posting error. Decorating supplies should have been posted as decorating services.		

Task 12

Refer to the following bank statement.

(a) Enter the bank charges (no VAT) and rates (no VAT) which have not yet been accounted for.

(b) Reconcile the bank statement and save a screenshot of the bank reconciliation screen showing reconciled items. Save this as Evidence 6. If the bank statement does not reconcile, check your work and make the necessary corrections.

MAIN STREET BANK PLC

Statement of account

Main Street Bank plc
25 Main Street
Arnold
AF6 8NG

Account
Dolby Decorating
610 Wheatley Street
Moorhall
East Arnold
EF1 5KM

Account number: 85426474
Sort code: 20-87-36

Date: 31 March 20-X

Date	Details	Debit £	Credit £	Balance £	
01-Mar	Opening balance			−3460.00	D
03-Mar	020783	50.00		−3510.00	D
05-Mar	BACS Bingham Housing		12404.40	8894.40	C
10-Mar	BACS Limegate		1591.20	10485.60	C
18-Mar	DD TK Telephones	100.80		10384.80	C
19-Mar	Credit 10650		519.00	10903.80	C
20-Mar	STO Moorhall Rentals	127.20		10776.60	C
21-Mar	Cash withdrawal	175.00		10601.60	C
25-Mar	BACS Walker	1737.22		8864.38	C
26-Mar	020784	1500.00		7364.38	C
26-Mar	DD Arnold City Council	130.00		7234.38	C
27-Mar	BACS Limegate		1605.95	8840.33	C
30-Mar	020785	4900.50		3939.83	C
30-Mar	BACS Wages	4980.00		−1040.17	D
31-Mar	Bank charges	18.00		−1058.17	D

D = Debit   C = Credit

Task 13

Documentation of evidence

You are now required to generate the following documents to demonstrate your competence:

Document and reports	Save/print as:
A document showing all transactions with each customer during March 20-X	**Evidence 1a – Name – AAT number**
A document showing the balance owed by each customer as at 31 March 20-X	**Evidence 1b – Name – AAT number**
The following information must be evidenced within these documents: • *Customer name* • *Account code* • *Payment terms*	*Depending on your software, you may need to save/print one or more documents*
A document showing all transactions with each supplier during March 20-X	**Evidence 2a – Name – AAT number**
A document showing the balance owed by each supplier as at 31 March 20-X	**Evidence 2b – Name – AAT number**
The following information must be evidenced within these documents: • *Supplier name* • *Account code* • *Payment terms*	*Depending on your software, you may need to save/print one or more documents*
An audit trail, showing full details of all transactions, including details of receipts/payments allocated to items in customer/supplier accounts and details of items in the bank account that have been reconciled	**Evidence 3a – Name – AAT number**
Petty cash account in the nominal ledger accounts, showing all transactions within the account	**Evidence 3b – Name – AAT number**
Trial balance as at 31 March 20-X	**Evidence 4 – Name – AAT number**
Screenshot of the recurring entry set up screen, including all relevant input detail	**Evidence 5 – Name – AAT number**
Screenshot of the bank reconciliation screen showing reconciled items	**Evidence 6 – Name – AAT number**

Note that the accounting package you are using may not use exactly the same report names as those shown above.

Before you finish your work use the checklist below to make sure you have printed all documents and reports as specified in the assessment.

Checklist

Documents and reports	Task	X when printed
Screenshot of the recurring entry set up screen, including all relevant input detail	13	
Screenshot of the bank reconciliation screen showing reconciled items	13	
A document showing all transactions with each customer during March 20-X	13	
A document showing the balance owed by each customer as at 31 March 20-X	13	
A document showing all transactions with each supplier during March 20-X	13	
A document showing the balance owed by each supplier as at 31 March 20-X	13	
An audit trail, showing full details of all transactions, including details of receipts/payments allocated to items in customer/supplier accounts and details of items in the bank account that have been reconciled	13	
Trial balance as at 31 March 20-X	13	
Petty cash account within the nominal ledger, showing all transactions within the account	13	

Practice assessment 3
Clifton Card Warehouse

Instructions to candidates

This assessment asks you to input data into a computerised accounting package and produce documents and reports. There are 13 tasks and it is important that you attempt all tasks.

The time allowed to complete this computerised accounting assessment is **2 hours, plus 15 minutes reading time**.

Additional time up to a maximum of 1 hour may be scheduled by your tutor to allow for delays due to computer issues such as printer queues.

It is important that you print **all** reports and documents specified in the tasks so your work can be assessed. A checklist has been provided at the end of the assessment to help you check that all documents and reports have been printed.

If your computerised accounting system allows for the generation of PDFs, these can be generated instead of hard copy prints. Screenshots saved as image files are also acceptable.

Data

Clifton Card Warehouse is an existing business that supplies cards, gift wrap and decorations to shops across the region. The owner is **Nathan Pearson** who operates as a sole trader.

The business has previously kept manual books but from **1 July 20-X**, the accounts are to be computerised.

You are employed as an Accounts Assistant.

You can assume that all documentation has been checked for accuracy and authorised by Nathan Pearson.

Cash and credit sales are analysed in **four** ways:
- Greetings cards
- Gift wrap
- Decorations
- Online sales

All stock is stored in a rented unit, where goods are despatched from. Nathan likes to analyse his purchases as follows:
- purchases – gift cards
- purchases – decorations/gift wrap

Some nominal ledger accounts have already been allocated account codes. You may need to amend account names or create other account codes.

The business is registered for VAT (Standard Accounting). The rate of VAT charged on all goods and services sold by Clifton Card Warehouse is 20%.

All expenditure should be analysed as you feel appropriate.

Before you start you should:
- Set the financial year to start on **1 July of the current year**.
- Set the software date as **31 July of the current year**.
- Set up the company details by entering the name **Clifton Card Warehouse** and the address: **340 Briarwood Road, Granby, GD7 6CA**. In a training environment you should add your name after the business name to identify your printouts.
- The VAT number is 542 2478 12 and the standard rate VAT of 20% is charged on all sales.

Task 1

(a)   Set up customer records for each of the customers with opening balances as at 1 July 20-X.

Customer Account Code: AGC01
Company name: Ashford Gift Centre
Address: 50 Leahurst Road, Limely Bridge, LW6 4WJ
Contact name: Phoebe May
Telephone: 0145 652798
Payment terms: 30 days
Credit limit: £5,200.00
Opening balance: £4,210.32

Customer Account Code: BGC01
Company name: Brooklane Garden Centre
Address: 125 Woodbank Lane, Limely Bridge, LK5 1VI
Contact name: Sarah Miller
Telephone: 0145 758201
Payment terms: 30 days
Credit limit: £7,500.00
Opening balance: £262.50

Customer Account Code: CC01
Company name: Cossall Cards
Address: 68 Granby Road, Granby, GB1 4KL
Contact name: Agnes Nowak
Telephone: 0152 415234
Payment terms: 30 days
Credit limit: £3,000.00
Opening balance: £1,798.75

Customer Account Code: MP01
Company name: Michelle Proctor Ltd
Address: 414 Cardale Road, Granby, GB7 5RD
Contact name: Raj Singh
Telephone: 0152 778995
Payment terms: 30 days
Credit limit: £9,700.00
Opening balance: £3,475.20

(b)   Generate a customer activity report on screen. Check it for accuracy and, if necessary, correct any errors. You do not need to print the customer activity report.

Task 2

(a) Set up supplier records for each of the suppliers with opening balances as at 1 July 20-X.

Supplier Account Code: BW01

Company name: Burton Wholesale

Address: 57 Ged Drive, Chadderdale, CH7 4KU

Contact name: Priya Malik

Telephone: 0123 142124

Payment terms: 30 days

Credit limit: £12,300.00

Opening balance: £6,203.00

Supplier Account Code: JFCS01

Company name: JF Card Supplies

Address: 144 Standhill Parkway, Buxton Road, Chadderdale, CH2 4TF

Contact name: Jasmin Fisher

Telephone: 0123 872365

Payment terms: 30 days

Credit limit: £7,500.00

Opening balance: £2,004.24

Supplier Account Code: SCS01

Company name: Stonebridge Card Supplies

Address: 48 Hilton Road, Chadderdale, CH6 5YR

Contact name: Samia Masood

Telephone: 0123 874215

Payment terms: 30 days

Credit limit: £3,000.00

Opening balance: £741.00

Supplier Account Code: WW01

Company name: Woolerton Warehouse

Address: Unit 23, Colwick Parkway, Parkdale Road, Granby, GB4 9IO

Contact name: Emilie Durand

Telephone: 0152 748214

Payment terms: 30 days

Credit limit: £11,000.00

Opening balance: £6,410.00

(b) Generate a supplier activity report on screen. Check it for accuracy and, if necessary, correct any errors. You do not need to print the supplier activity report.

Task 3

(a) Using the list of nominal ledger balances below, set up nominal ledger records for each account. Select, amend or create nominal ledger codes where required.

(b) Generate a trial balance on screen. Check it for accuracy and, if necessary, correct any errors. You do not need to print the trial balance.

Opening Trial Balance as at 1 July 20-X

Account name	Note	Debit £	Credit £
Bank		4,840.20	
Bank deposit		6,000.00	
Petty cash		50.00	
Furniture – cost		34,650.00	
Furniture – accumulated depreciation			5,197.50
Sales ledger control account	1	9,746.77	
Purchase ledger control account	1		15,358.24
VAT on sales	2		8,780.00
VAT on purchases	2	1,640.00	
Capital			27,591.23
Sales – Greetings cards	3		NIL
Sales – Gift wrap	3		NIL
Sales – Decorations	3		NIL
Sales – Online sales	3		NIL
Bank interest received	3		NIL
General rates	3	NIL	
Purchases (Gift cards)	3	NIL	
Purchases (Decorations/Gift wrap)	3	NIL	
Bank charges	3	NIL	
Donations	3	NIL	
Cleaning	3	NIL	
Office stationery	3	NIL	
Travel and subsistence	3	NIL	
Advertising	3	NIL	
Totals		56,926.97	56,926.97

Notes:

1   As you have already entered opening balances for customers and suppliers you may not need to enter these balances, you will need to check whether your accounting software requires you to make a separate adjustment.

2   The accounting software you are using may not require you to post these balances individually. The opening balance on the account is £7,140.00 (credit) if posting as a single brought forward balance.

3   These nominal accounts are needed for transactions taking place in July 20-X.

In the rest of the assessment, you will only make entries to the nominal ledger accounts you created in Task 3. You will not be required to make entries to any accounts other than those you have already created.

Task 4

Enter the following sales invoices and sales credit notes into the computer.

Sales Invoice

INVOICE

Clifton Card Warehouse

340 Briarwood Road, Granby, GD7 6CA

FAO: Phoebe May
Ashford Gift Centre
50 Leahurst Road
Limely Bridge
LW6 4WJ

invoice no   **00895**

date   **2 July 20-X**

Item	Quantity	Total
Rolls of wrapping paper @ 40p per roll	160	£64.00
Packs of blue balloons @ 20p per pack	250	£50.00
Packs of helium balloons @ £1.20 per pack	500	£600.00
	total	£714.00
	VAT @ 20%	**£142.80**
	Total invoice	**£856.80**

VAT registration number 542 2478 12

Sales Invoice

━━━━━━━━━━━━━━━━━ **INVOICE** ━━━━━━━━━━━━━━━━━

Clifton Card Warehouse

340 Briarwood Road, Granby, GD7 6CA

FAO: Raj Singh
Michelle Proctor Ltd
414 Cardale Road
Granby
GB7 5RD

invoice no   **00896**

date   **6 July 20-X**

Item	Quantity	Total
Assorted greetings cards @ £0.62 per card	5000	£3,100.00
Banners @ £0.80 per banner	75	£60.00
	total	**£3,160.00**
	VAT @ 20%	**£632.00**
	Total invoice	**£3,792.00**

VAT registration number 542 2478 12

Sales Invoice

━━━━━━━━━━━━━━━━━ **INVOICE** ━━━━━━━━━━━━━━━━━

Clifton Card Warehouse

340 Briarwood Road, Granby, GD7 6CA

FAO: Sarah Miller
Brooklane Garden Centre
125 Woodbank Lane
Limely Bridge
LK5 1VI

invoice no   **00897**

date   **6 July 20-X**

Item	Quantity	Total
Candles @ £0.60 each	205	£123.00
Table decorations @ £2.50 each	110	£275.00
Assorted greetings cards @ £2.20 each	300	£660.00
	total	**£1,058.00**
	VAT @ 20%	**£211.60**
	Total invoice	**£1,269.60**

VAT registration number 542 2478 12

Sales Credit Note

CREDIT NOTE

Clifton Card Warehouse

340 Briarwood Road, Granby, GD7 6CA

FAO: Agnes Nowak Cossall Cards 68 Granby Road Granby GB1 4KL	credit note no **0074** date **8 July 20-X**

Item	Quantity	Total
Damaged greetings cards returned @ £2.20 each	10	£22.00
	total	£22.00
	VAT @ 20%	£4.40
	Total credit note	£26.40

VAT registration number 542 2478 12

Task 5

Using the information from the purchases day book and purchase returns day book below, enter these transactions into the computer.

Date 20-X	Supplier	Invoice number	Gross	VAT	Net	Gift cards	Decorations /Gift wrap
03-Jul	JF Card Supplies	INV 3079	5125.55	854.26	4271.29	427.29	3844.00
10-Jul	Woolerton Warehouse	WW 417	3564.06	594.01	2970.05	2970.05	0.00
12-Jul	Stonebridge Card Supplies	1784	1600.08	266.68	1333.40	0.00	1333.40
13-Jul	Woolerton Warehouse	32546	649.56	108.26	541.30	200.00	341.30
	Totals		10939.25	1823.21	9116.04	3597.34	5518.70

Date 20-X	Supplier	Credit note	Gross	VAT	Net	Gift cards	Decorations /Gift wrap
14-Jul	Stonebridge Card Supplies	CN41	209.06	34.84	174.22	74.22	100.00
16-Jul	Burton Wholesale	36	69.36	11.56	57.80	0.00	57.80
	Totals		278.42	46.40	232.02	74.22	157.80

Task 6

(a)   Clifton Card Warehouse also have online sales. All payments made by customers are done through a secure online payment system called CashQuick.

CashQuick make payments to Clifton Card Warehouse at the of end each week using 'Faster Payments'

Enter the following 'Online cash sales listing' receipts into the accounting software.

Week ending	Amount received from CashQuick (including VAT at the standard rate) £
8 July 20-X	3,602.70
15 July 20-X	3,297.60
22 July 20-X	1,896.00
29 July 20-X	2,941.20

(b)   Enter the following cash purchases into the computer.

Date 20-X	Payment method	Details	Amount
10 July	Cheque no: 024226	Farnborough Furniture – Purchase of assets – display table and shelving	£1,340.00 including VAT
14 July	Cheque no: 024227	Cromford Cards – Selection of greetings cards for resale	£299.00 including VAT
16 July	Cheque no: 024228	Full page article in the Granby News advertising Clifton Card Warehouse	£642.00 plus VAT

Task 7

(a)   Enter the following BACS payments received from customers into the computer.

BACS payments received listing

Date	Customer name	Amount £	Details
10 July	Michelle Proctor Ltd	3,475.20	Payment of opening balance
13 July	Cossall Cards	1,772.35	Payment of opening balance less credit note 0074 for £26.40
14 July	Ashford Gift Centre	4,210.32	Payment of opening balance
30 July	Ashford Gift Centre	1,200.00	Payment on account

(b)   Enter the following cheque received into the computer.

Cheque payments received listing

Date	Customer name	Amount £	Details
24 July	Brooklane Garden Centre	1,269.60	Invoice 00897

(c)   Print a statement of account for Michelle Proctor Ltd dated 31 July 20-X, showing all transactions that have taken place during the month.

Task 8

Enter the following payments to suppliers into the computer.

Cheque stubs

Date 22/07/-X **Pay** Stonebridge Card Supplies £2,132.02 024229	To pay the balance as at 1 July and invoice 1784, less credit note CN41

Date 23/07/-X **Pay** Burton Wholesale £6,203.00 024230	To pay the balance as at 1 July

Date 23/07/-X **Pay** Woolerton Warehouse £6,410.00 024231	To pay the balance as at 1 July

Task 9

(a) You have received the following email. Set up this recurring entry into the computer but do not process the first payment.

Email	
To:	Accounts Assistant
From:	Nathan Pearson
Date:	3 July 20-X
Subject:	Recurring entry for business rates from Granby Council

Hello

I have received confirmation today that the business rates will be £123.40 per month to be taken by direct debit out of the bank account on the 15th of the month for 12 months. Please can you set up a recurring entry? VAT is not applicable.

Kind regards

Nathan

(b) Print/save a screenshot of the screen setting up the recurring entry. Save this as Evidence 5a.

(c) You have received the following email regarding an error in yesterday's email. Edit the recurring entry.

Email	
To:	Accounts Assistant
From:	Nathan Pearson
Date:	4 July 20-X
Subject:	Error in my email dated 3 July regarding recurring entry

Hello

Apologies, it would appear I emailed you the incorrect amount yesterday for the business rates direct debit. The amount should be for £132.40 per month, still to be taken on the 15th of each month but it should only be for 10 months. Please can you amend the recurring entry? VAT is not applicable.

Kind regards

Nathan

(d) Print/save a screenshot of the screen showing the amended recurring entry. Save this as Evidence 5b.

(e) Process the first payment for the direct debit.

Task 10

(a) Enter the following petty cash vouchers into the computer.

petty cash voucher		Number 054

date   5 July 20-X

description	amount

	£	p
Cleaning materials (VAT included)	12	20
	12	20
Receipt attached		

Signature ... *T Litchfield*

Authorised *N Pearson*

petty cash voucher		Number 055

date   6 July 20-X

description	amount

	£	p
Donation to local charity (No VAT)	15	00
	15	00
Receipt attached		

Signature ... *L Moore*

Authorised *N Pearson*

petty cash voucher

Number 056

date 10 July 20-X

description	amount	
	£	p
Train ticket to promotional event (No VAT)	14	80
	14	80
Receipt attached		

Signature *L Moore*

Authorised *N Pearson*

petty cash voucher

Number 057

date 10 July 20-X

description	amount	
	£	p
Pack of printer paper	5	20
VAT	1	04
	6	24
Receipt attached		

Signature *T Litchfield*

Authorised *N Pearson*

(b) A petty cash reimbursement request has been received. Enter this information into the computer.

PETTY CASH REIMBURSEMENT FORM
Date: 11 July 20-X
Amount: £48.24
Cheque payable to: cash
Cheque number: 024225
Details: Restore the petty cash account
Signed: *N Pearson*

Task 11

Enter the following journal into the computer.

Journal entry 012 30 July 20-X	Dr	Cr
Office equipment	3,748.00	
Furniture		3,748.00
Correction of posting error. Office equipment incorrectly posted to the furniture account.		

Task 12

Refer to the following bank statement. Using the accounting software and the transactions you have already posted:

(a) Enter any additional items on the bank statement that have not yet been recorded into the accounting software (ignore VAT on any of these transactions).

(b) Reconcile the bank statement and save a screenshot of the bank reconciliation screen showing reconciled items. Save this as Evidence 6. If the bank statement does not reconcile, check your work and make the necessary corrections.

HIGHFIELD BUILDING SOCIETY

Statement of account

Highfield Building Society
126 Granby Road
Granby
GB6 8TS

Account
Clifton Card Warehouse
340 Briarwood Road
Granby
GD7 6CA

Account: 21475894

Sort code: 23-24-74

Date: 31 July 20-X

Date	Details	Debit £	Credit £	Balance £	
01-Jul	Opening balance			4840.20	C
05-Jul	BACS Ashford Gift Centre		856.80	5697.00	C
08-Jul	FP CashQuick		3602.70	9299.70	C
10-Jul	BACS Michelle Proctor		3475.20	12774.90	C
13-Jul	Cossall Cards		1772.35	14547.25	C
14-Jul	BACS Ashford Gift Centre		4210.32	18757.57	C
15-Jul	DD Granby Council - Rates	132.40		18625.17	C
15-Jul	FP CashQuick		3297.60	21922.77	C
16-Jul	024225	48.24		21874.53	C
18-Jul	024226	1340.00		20534.53	C
19-Jul	024227	299.00		20235.53	C
21-Jul	024228	770.40		19465.13	C
22-Jul	FP CashQuick		1896.00	21361.13	C
27-Jul	024229	2132.02		19229.11	C
28-Jul	024230	6203.00		13026.11	C
29-Jul	FP CashQuick		2941.20	15967.31	C
29-Jul	Credit 10750		1269.60	17236.91	C
30-Jul	BACS Ashford Gift Centre		1200.00	18436.91	C
30-Jul	Bank charges	22.00		18414.91	C
	D = Debit C = Credit				

Task 13

Documentation of evidence

You are now required to generate the following documents to demonstrate your competence

Document and reports	Save/print as:
A document showing all transactions with each customer during July 20-X	**Evidence 1a – Name – AAT number**
A document showing the balance owed by each customer as at 31 July 20-X	**Evidence 1b – Name – AAT number**
The following information must be evidenced within these documents:	*Depending on your software, you may need to save/print one or more documents*
• *Customer name*	**Evidence 1c – Name – AAT number**
• *Account code*	
• *Payment terms*	
A document showing all transactions with each supplier during July 20-X	**Evidence 2a – Name – AAT number**
A document showing the balance owed by each supplier as at 31 July 20-X	**Evidence 2b – Name – AAT number**
The following information must be evidenced within these documents:	*Depending on your software, you may need to save/print one or more documents*
• *Supplier name*	
• *Account code*	
• *Payment terms*	
An audit trail, showing full details of all transactions, including details of receipts/payments allocated to items in customer/supplier accounts and details of items in the bank account that have been reconciled	**Evidence 3 – Name – AAT number**
Trial balance as at 31 July 20-X	**Evidence 4 – Name – AAT number**
Screenshot of the recurring entry set up screens, including all relevant input detail	**Evidence 5a – Name – AAT number** **Evidence 5b – Name – AAT number**
Screenshot of the bank reconciliation screen showing reconciled items	**Evidence 6 – Name – AAT number**

Note that the accounting package you are using may not use exactly the same report names as those shown above.

Before you finish your work use the checklist below to make sure you have printed all documents and reports as specified in the assessment.

Checklist

Documents and reports	Task	X when printed
Screenshot of the recurring entry set up screen, including all relevant input detail	13	
Screenshot of the **amended** recurring entry set up screen, including all relevant input detail	13	
Screenshot of the bank reconciliation screen showing reconciled items	13	
A document showing all transactions with each customer during July 20-X	13	
A document showing the balance owed by each customer as at 31 July 20-X	13	
A document showing all transactions with each supplier during July 20-X	13	
A document showing the balance owed by each supplier as at 31 July 20-X	13	
An audit trail, showing full details of all transactions, including details of receipts/payments allocated to items in customer/supplier accounts and details of items in the bank account that have been reconciled	13	
Trial balance as at 31 July 20-X	13	

Practice assessment 4
Southglade Stationery Warehouse

Instructions to candidates

This assessment asks you to input data into a computerised accounting package and produce documents and reports. There are 13 tasks and it is important that you attempt all tasks.

The time allowed to complete this computerised accounting assessment is **2 hours, plus 15 minutes reading time**.

Additional time up to a maximum of 1 hour may be scheduled by your tutor to allow for delays due to computer issues such as printer queues.

It is important that you print **all** reports and documents specified in the tasks so your work can be assessed. A checklist has been provided at the end of the assessment to help you check that all documents and reports have been printed.

If your computerised accounting system allows for the generation of PDFs, these can be generated instead of hard copy prints. Screenshots saved as image files are also acceptable.

Data

Southglade Stationery Warehouse has been trading for two years. They have recently expanded very quickly due to two large contracts to supply stationery items to local colleges. The owner is **Tanveer Mirza** who operates as a sole trader.

The business has previously kept manual books but from **1 August 20-X**, the accounts are to be computerised.

You are employed as an Accounting Technician.

You can assume that all documentation has been checked for accuracy and authorised by Tanveer Mirza.

Cash and credit sales are analysed in **four** ways:

- Ink

- Paper

- Filing and folders

- Online sales

Some nominal ledger accounts have already been allocated account codes. You may need to amend account names or create other account codes.

The business is registered for VAT (Standard Accounting). The rate of VAT charged on all goods and services sold by Southglade Stationery Warehouse is 20%.

All expenditure should be analysed as you feel appropriate.

Before you start you should:

- Set the financial year to start on **1 August of the current year**.

- Set the software date as **31 August of the current year**.

- Set up the company details by entering the name **Southglade Stationery Warehouse** and the address: **Unit 3, 810 Southglade Road, Newbridge, NE6 6RB**. In a training environment you should add your name after the business name to identify your printouts.

- The VAT number is 410 8796 07 and the standard rate VAT of 20% is charged on all sales.

Task 1

(a)   From the customer record cards below, enter the information to set up customer records.

Customer Account Code: FC01	**Customer Account Code:** FSS02
Company name: Farnsworth College	**Company name:** Fusion Stationery Supplies
Address: 179 Farnsfield Way, Newbridge, NB4 2QP	**Address:** 94 Bracebridge Road, Filey, FL6 1BD
Contact name: David Roberts	**Contact name:** Janet Spencer
Telephone: 0198 332113	**Telephone:** 0150 963424
Payment terms: 30 days	**Payment terms:** 30 days
Credit limit: £9,000.00	**Credit limit:** £22,000.00
Customer Account Code: NLC01	**Customer Account Code:** NC02
Company name: Newbridge Learning Centre	**Company name:** Northgate College
Address: 150 Northglade Road, Newbridge, NN2 1HB	**Address:** 36 Cromford Road, Filey, FW2 3GS
Contact name: Samuel Impellizzeri	**Contact name:** Lukasz Cservenyak
Telephone: 0198 213452	**Telephone:** 0150 077360
Payment terms: 30 days	**Payment terms:** 30 days
Credit limit: £8,250.00	**Credit limit:** £12,100.00

(b)   Enter the following opening balances into the customer records as at 1 August 20-X:

Farnsworth College	£6,542.20
Fusion Stationery	£3,339.90
Newbridge Learning Centre	£2,010.20
Northgate College	£7,542.00

(c)   Generate a customer activity report on screen. Check it for accuracy and, if necessary, correct any errors. You do not need to print the customer activity report.

Task 2

(a) From the supplier record cards below, enter the information to set up supplier records.

Supplier Account Code: ROS01 **Company name:** Riverside Office Supplies Ltd **Address:** 52 Riverside Way, Filey, FG1 2NP **Contact name:** Catherine Hemmingway **Telephone:** 0150 210210 **Payment terms:** 30 days **Credit limit:** £6,400.00

Supplier Account Code: SS01 **Company name:** Shelford Stationery **Address:** 243 Steinbeck Street, Sneinton, SD6 7HT **Contact name:** Louise Richards **Telephone:** 0197 113679 **Payment terms:** 30 days **Credit limit:** £22,000.00

Supplier Account Code: TKAS01 **Company name:** TKA Supplies **Address:** Unit 5, Yalding Industrial Estate, Newark, NE6 4AB **Contact name:** Tamara Tomlinson **Telephone:** 0121 669774 **Payment terms:** 30 days **Credit limit:** £5,500.00

Supplier Account Code: WSL01 **Company name:** Wilford & Son Ltd **Address:** 7 Strelley Lane, Filey, FY1 1LP **Contact name:** Ron Wilford **Telephone:** 0150 200300 **Payment terms:** 30 days **Credit limit:** £4,200.00

(b) Enter the following opening balances into the supplier records as at 1 August 20-X:

Riverside Office Supplies Ltd	£4,350.00
Shelford Stationery	£2,230.00
TKA Supplies	£3,740.60
Wilford & Son Ltd	£1,635.55

(c) Generate a supplier activity report on screen. Check it for accuracy and, if necessary, correct any errors. You do not need to print the supplier activity report.

Task 3

(a) Using the list of nominal ledger balances below, set up nominal ledger records for each account. Select, amend or create nominal ledger codes where required.

(b) Generate a trial balance on screen. Check it for accuracy and, if necessary, correct any errors. You do not need to print the trial balance.

Opening Trial Balance as at 1 August 20-X

Account name	Note	Debit £	Credit £
Bank			2,403.00
Petty cash		100.00	
Motor vehicles – cost		8,730.50	
Motor vehicles – accumulated depreciation			1,746.10
Office equipment – cost		12,707.70	
Office equipment – accumulated depreciation			1,524.92
Sales ledger control account	1	19,434.30	
Purchase ledger control account	1		11,956.15
VAT on sales	2		6,502.40
VAT on purchases	2	1,870.46	
Capital			18,710.39
Loan	3		NIL
Sales – Ink	3		NIL
Sales – Paper	3		NIL
Sales – Filing and folders	3		NIL
Sales – Online sales	3		NIL
Rent Income	3		NIL
Bank deposit	3	NIL	
Drawings	3	NIL	
Materials purchased	3	NIL	
Telephone	3	NIL	
Advertising	3	NIL	
Drawings	3	NIL	
Postage and Carriage	3	NIL	
Office machine maintenance	3	NIL	
Repairs and renewals	3	NIL	
Bank charges	3	NIL	
Miscellaneous expenses	3	NIL	
Totals		42,842.96	42,842.96

Notes:

1   As you have already entered opening balances for customers and suppliers you may not need to enter these balances, you will need to check whether your accounting software requires you to make a separate adjustment.

2   The accounting software you are using may not require you to post these balances individually. The opening balance on the account is £4,631.94 (credit) if posting as a single brought forward balance.

3   These nominal accounts are needed for transactions taking place in August 20-X.

In the rest of the assessment, you will only make entries to the nominal ledger accounts you created in Task 3. You will not be required to make entries to any accounts other than those you have already created.

Task 4

Enter the following sales invoices and sales credit notes into the computer.

Sales Invoice

━━━━━━━━━━━━━━━━━━━ **INVOICE** ━━━━━━━━━━━━━━━━━━━
Southglade Stationery Warehouse
Unit 3, 810 Southglade Road, Newbridge, NE6 6RB

FAO: Lukasz Cservenyak	invoice no	**007140**
Northgate College		
36 Cromford Road	date	**2 August 20-X**
Filey		
FW2 3GS		

Item	Quantity	Total
Boxes of A5 folders @ £2.50 per box	150	£375.00
Packs of A4 plain copier paper @ £3.50 per pack	364	£1,274.00
A4 Lever arch folders @ £4.20 per folder	500	£2,100.00
	total	**£3,749.00**
	VAT @ 20%	**£749.80**
	Total invoice	**£4,498.80**

VAT registration number 410 8796 07

Sales Credit Note

━━━━━━━━━━━━━━━━━━━ **CREDIT NOTE** ━━━━━━━━━━━━━━━━━━━
Southglade Stationery Warehouse
Unit 3, 810 Southglade Road, Newbridge, NE6 6RB

FAO: David Roberts	credit note no	**047**
Farnsworth College		
179 Farnsfield Way	date	**6 August 20-X**
Newbridge		
NB4 2QP		

Item	Quantity	Total
Faulty ink cartridges returned @ £14.50 per ink cartridge	12	£174.00
Damaged lever arch folders returned @ £4.20 per folder	5	£21.00
	total	**£195.00**
	VAT @ 20%	**£39.00**
	Total credit note	**£234.00**

VAT registration number 410 8796 07

Sales Invoice

─── INVOICE ───
Southglade Stationery Warehouse
Unit 3, 810 Southglade Road, Newbridge, NE6 6RB

FAO: Janet Spencer
Fusion Stationery Supplies
94 Bracebridge Road
Filey
FL6 1BD

invoice no   **007141**

date   **14 August 20-X**

Item	Quantity	Total
Packs of A4 blue paper @ £2.99 per pack	20	£59.80
Packs of A4 green paper @ £2.99 per pack	20	£59.80
Document wallets @ £0.60 each	350	£210.00
Ink cartridges @ £44.60 per pack	50	£2,230.00
	total	£2,559.60
	VAT @ 20%	£511.92
	Total invoice	£3,071.52

VAT registration number 410 8796 07

Sales Credit Note

─── CREDIT NOTE ───
Southglade Stationery Warehouse
Unit 3, 810 Southglade Road, Newbridge, NE6 6RB

FAO: Lukasz Cservenyak
Northgate College
36 Cromford Road
Filey
FW2 3GS

credit note no   **048**

date   **16 August 20-X**

Item	Quantity	Total
Boxes of A5 folders @ £2.50 per box returned	7	£17.50
Packs of A4 plain copier paper @ £3.50 per pack returned	13	£45.50
	total	£63.00
	VAT @ 20%	£12.60
	Total credit note	£75.60

VAT registration number 410 8796 07

Task 5

Enter the following purchase invoices and purchase credit note into the computer. Ensure that you read any additional notes from Tanveer regarding the invoices.

Purchase Invoice

INVOICE	**TKA Supplies**
	Unit 5, Yalding Industrial Estate, Newark, NE6 4AB
	VAT registration number 214 9784 14

Southglade Stationery Warehouse	invoice no	**INV635**
Unit 3		
810 Southglade Road	date	**8 August 20-X**
Newbridge		
NE6 6RB		

X2 Computers @ £580.60 each	£1,161.20
VAT @ 20%	£232.24
Total invoice	**£1,393.44**

Hi,
When posting this invoice please note that the computers are for use in our accounts office and should be coded as non-current assets.
Regards
Tanveer

Purchase Invoice

Wilford & Son Ltd	INVOICE
7 Strelley Lane, Filey, FY1 1LP	
VAT registration number 478 4398 03	

Southglade Stationery Warehouse	invoice no	**6310**
Unit 3		
810 Southglade Road	date	**9 August 20-X**
Newbridge		
NE6 6RB		

X3 Filing cabinet locks @ £2.30 each	£6.90
X4 Promotional stands for advertising @ £87.99 each	£351.96
	£358.86
VAT @ 20%	£71.77
Total invoice	**£430.63**

Hi,
When posting this invoice please note that these items are not for resale and therefore should not be posted to purchases. You will need to code them as overheads.
Regards, Tanveer

Purchase Invoice

INVOICE
Shelford Stationery
243 Steinbeck Street, Sneinton, SD6 7HT

Southglade Stationery Warehouse Unit 3 810 Southglade Road Newbridge NE6 6RB	invoice no	**012012**
	date	**11 August 20-X**

Goods for resale	£15,740.30
VAT @ 20%	£3,148.06
Total invoice	**£18,888.36**

VAT registration number 457 1302 80

Purchase Credit Note

CREDIT NOTE
Shelford Stationery
243 Steinbeck Street, Sneinton, SD6 7HT

Southglade Stationery Warehouse Unit 3 810 Southglade Road Newbridge NE6 6RB	credit note no	**124**
	date	**15 August 20-X**

Damaged goods for resale returned	£3,541.20
VAT @ 20%	£708.24
Total credit note	**£4,249.44**

VAT registration number 457 1302 80

Task 6

(a)   Southglade Stationery Warehouse also have online sales. All payments made by customers are done through a secure online payment system called CashLinkOnline.

CashLinkOnline make payments to Southglade Stationery Warehouse at the end of each week using 'Faster Payments'

Enter the following 'Online cash sales listing' receipts into the accounting software.

Week ending	Amount received from CashLinkOnline (including VAT at the standard rate) £
5 August 20-X	6,595.20
12 August 20-X	5,009.16
19 August 20-X	4,802.40
26 August 20-X	3,528.00

(b)   Enter the following cash purchases into the computer.

Cash purchases listing

Date 20-X	Payment method	Details	Amount
14 August	Cheque no: 201634	Advert in Southglade Times to advertise for a new member of staff.	£690.00 including VAT
30 August	Cheque no: 201636	Payment to Thorpe Telephones to pay a telephone bill.	£78.00 including VAT

(c)   A cheque has been received for the goods sold below. Enter the cash sales receipt into the computer

Cash sales receipt

—————————————— **Receipt** ——————————————
Southglade Stationery Warehouse
Unit 3, 810 Southglade Road, Newbridge, NE6 6RB
VAT Reg no. 410 8796 07

Receipt no   **94**

date   **18 August 20-X**

	£
X200 A4 folders @ £1.99 each	
Total (Including VAT)	398.00

(d) You have received the following email. Enter this transaction into the computer.

Email	
To:	Accounting Technician
From:	Tanveer Mirza
Date:	13 August 20-X
Subject:	Bank Loan received

Hi

Today the business has received a bank loan of £20,000 into the current account.

Please record this transaction. VAT is not applicable.

Kind regards

Tanveer

(e) You have received the following email. Enter this transaction into the computer.

Email	
To:	Accounting Technician
From:	Tanveer Mirza
Date:	27 August 20-X
Subject:	Bank transfer

Hello

I have arranged a transfer from the bank current account to the deposit account for £15,000.

Please record this transaction. VAT is not applicable.

Kind regards

Tanveer

Task 7

(a) Enter the following cheques received into the computer.

Newbridge Building Society
96 Glaisdale Road
Newbridge, NB5 3MK

Date   20 August 20-X

Pay: Southglade Stationery Warehouse

Eleven thousand, nine hundred and sixty five pounds

and twenty pence only

£ 11,965.20

A/c payee only

L Cservenyak

Northgate College

321024   65712463   30-87-74

NB: To pay the balance as at 1 August and invoice 007140, less credit note 048

Arnold Bank
14 Parkdale Road
Arnold, AJ1 4FB

Date   21 August 20-X

Pay: Southglade Stationery Warehouse

Two thousand and ten pounds and twenty

pence only

£ 2,010.20

A/c payee only

Samuel Impellizzeri

Newbridge Learning Centre

217362   58931471   32-87-96

NB: To pay the balance as at 1 August

(b) Enter the following BACS payments received from customers into the computer.

BACS payments received listing

Date 20-X	Customer name	Amount £	Details
12 August	Farnsworth College	6,308.20	Payment of opening balance less credit note number 047
12 August	Fusion Stationery Supplies	3,339.90	Payment of opening balance
18 August	Fusion Stationery Supplies	2,400.00	Payment on account

Task 8

(a) Enter the following payments to suppliers into the computer.

BACS Payments to suppliers

Date 20-X	Supplier	Type	£	Details
22 August	Riverside Office Supplies Ltd	BACS	4,350.00	Payment of opening balance
22 August	Shelford Stationery	BACS	16,868.92	Pays opening balance and invoice 012012 less credit note 124
22 August	Wilford & Son Ltd	BACS	5,000.00	Payment on account

Cheque stub

Date 14/08/-X

Pay
TKA Supplies

£5,134.04

201635

NB: To pay the balance as at 1 August and invoice INV635

(b) Print a remitance advice for the payment to Riverside Office Supplies Ltd.

Task 9

Refer to the email below.

(a)   Set up recurring entries for the transactions.

(b)   Print a screenshot of the screen setting up each of the recurring entries. Save these as Evidence 5a and Evidence 5b.

(c)   Process the first payment for each standing order and direct debit.

Email	
To:	Accounting Technician
From:	Tanveer Mirza
Date:	22 August 20-X
Subject:	New direct debits and standing orders to be set up

Hello

Please can you set up a monthly direct debit for a maintenance contract for the photocopier. The payment will be to PH Photocopiers for £72.60 plus VAT per month for 10 months. This will be taken from the business bank account on the 24th of the month.

Can you also set up a standing order for rental income as we will be renting out the building next door to Harris Removals for £320.00 plus VAT per month for 6 months. This needs to be set up for the 25th of each month.

Kind regards

Tanveer

Task 10

(a)   A petty cash reimbursement request has been received. Enter this information into the computer.

PETTY CASH REIMBURSEMENT FORM
Date: 2 August 20-X
Amount: £50.00
Cheque payable to: Cash
Cheque number: 201633
Details: Restore the petty cash account
Signed: *7 Mirza*

(b)   Enter the following petty cash vouchers into the computer.

petty cash voucher		Number PC301
	date	2 August 20-X
description		amount

description	£	p
Stamps (No VAT)	6	36
	6	36
Receipt attached		

Signature   *N Sharpe*

Authorised   *7 Mirza*

petty cash voucher

Number PC302

date   5 August 20-X

description	amount	
	£	p
1000 plastic cups for the water machine in reception	22	10
VAT	4	42
	26	52
Receipt attached		

Signature ...... *N Sharpe* ....

Authorised ... *T Mirza* ....

---

petty cash voucher

Number PC303

date   8 August 20-X

description	amount	
	£	p
Plants for reception (VAT included)	8	30
	8	30
Receipt attached		

Signature ...... *N Sharpe* ....

Authorised ... *T Mirza* ....

Task 11

Enter the following journals into the computer.

Journal entry 017 12 August 20-X	Dr	Cr
Sales – Ink	64.80	
Sales – Filing and folders		64.80
Correction of posting error. Folders should have been posted to Filing and folders.		

Journal entry 018 20 August 20-X	Dr	Cr
Drawings	350.00	
Materials purchased		350.00
Items purchased by Tanveer Mirza for personal use.		

Task 12

Refer to the following bank statement. Using the accounting software and the transactions you have already posted:

(a)   Enter any additional items on the bank statement that have not yet been recorded into the accounting software (ignore VAT on any of these transactions).

(b)   Reconcile the bank statement and save a screenshot of the bank reconciliation screen showing reconciled items. Save this as Evidence 6. If the bank statement does not reconcile, check your work and make the necessary corrections.

ARNOLD BANK

Statement of account

Arnold Bank
14 Parkdale Road
Arnold
AJ1 4FB

Account
Southglade Stationery Warehouse
Unit 3, 810 Southglade Road
Newbridge
NE6 6RB

Account: 58946421
Sort code: 32-87-96

Date: 31 August 20-X

Date 20-X	Details	Debit £	Credit £	Balance £	
01-Aug	Opening balance			-2403.00	D
02-Aug	201633	50.00		-2453.00	D
05-Aug	FPCashLinkOnline		6595.20	4142.20	C
12-Aug	FPCashLinkOnline		5009.16	9151.36	C
12-Aug	BACS Farnsworth College		6308.20	15459.56	C
12-Aug	BACS Fusion Stationery		3339.90	18799.46	C
13-Aug	Loan		20000.00	38799.46	C
18-Aug	BACS Fusion Stationery		2400.00	41199.46	C
19-Aug	FPCashLinkOnline		4802.40	46001.86	C
19-Aug	201634	690.00		45311.86	C
22-Aug	BACS (multiple beneficiary)	26218.92		19092.94	C
23-Aug	201635	5134.04		13958.90	C
23-Aug	Credit 102119		398.00	14356.90	C
24-Aug	DD PH Photocopiers	87.12		14269.78	C
25-Aug	Credit 102120		11965.20	26234.98	C
25-Aug	SO Harris Removals		384.00	26618.98	C
26-Aug	FPCashLinkOnline		3528.00	30146.98	C
26-Aug	Credit 102121		2010.20	32157.18	C
27-Aug	Transfer to 58967412	15000.00		17157.18	C
30-Aug	Bank Charges	40.00		17117.18	C

D = Debit   C = Credit

Task 13

Documentation of evidence

You are now required to generate the following documents to demonstrate your competence:

Document and reports	Save/print as:
A document showing all transactions with each customer during August 20-X	**Evidence 1a – Name – AAT number**
A document showing the balance owed by each customer as at 31 August 20-X	**Evidence 1b – Name – AAT number**
The following information must be evidenced within these documents: • *Customer name* • *Account code* • *Payment terms*	*Depending on your software, you may need to save/print one or more documents*
A document showing all transactions with each supplier during August 20-X	**Evidence 2a – Name – AAT number**
A document showing the balance owed by each supplier as at 31 August 20-X	**Evidence 2b – Name – AAT number**
A remittance advice for Riverside Office Supplies Ltd	**Evidence 2c – Name – AAT number**
The following information must be evidenced within these documents: • *Supplier name* • *Account code* • *Payment terms*	*Depending on your software, you may need to save/print one or more documents*
An audit trail, showing full details of all transactions, including details of receipts/payments allocated to items in customer/supplier accounts and details of items in the bank account that have been reconciled	**Evidence 3 – Name – AAT number**
Trial balance as at 31 August 20-X	**Evidence 4 – Name – AAT number**
Screenshot of the recurring entry set up screen, including all relevant input detail	**Evidence 5 – Name – AAT number**
Screenshot of the bank reconciliation screen showing reconciled items	**Evidence 6 – Name – AAT number**

Note that the accounting package you are using may not use exactly the same report names as those shown above.

Before you finish your work use the checklist below to make sure you have printed all documents and reports as specified in the assessment.

Checklist

Documents and reports	Task	X when printed
Screenshot of the recurring entry set up screen, including all relevant input detail	13	
Screenshot of the bank reconciliation screen showing reconciled items	13	
A document showing all transactions with each customer during August 20-X	13	
A document showing the balance owed by each customer as at 31 August 20-X	13	
A document showing all transactions with each supplier during August 20-X	13	
A document showing the balance owed by each supplier as at 31 August 20-X	13	
An audit trail, showing full details of all transactions, including details of receipts/payments allocated to items in customer/supplier accounts and details of items in the bank account that have been reconciled	13	
Trial balance as at 31 August 20-X	13	
Remittance advice for Riverside Office Supplies	13	

Answers to practice assessment 1

Task	Transaction Type	Account(s)		Date 20-X	Net Amount £	VAT £	Allocated against receipt/ payment ✓	Reconciled with bank statement ✓
1	Customer O/bal	CRA001		1 Oct	4,304.40		✓	
	Customer O/bal	HOM001		1 Oct	650.50			
	Customer O/bal	SHI001		1 Oct	1,670.00		✓	
2	Supplier O/bal	CHR001		1 Oct	980.00			
	Supplier O/bal	EAS001		1 Oct	2,876.50		✓	
	Supplier O/bal	MAR001		1 Oct	940.55		✓	
3	Dr	Bank current account		1 Oct	16,000.00			✓
	Dr	Petty cash		1 Oct	160.00			
	Dr	Office equipment - cost		1 Oct	15,400.00			
	Cr	Office equipment – accumulated depreciation		1 Oct	3,080.00			
	Dr	Motor vehicles - cost		1 Oct	32,360.00			
	Cr	Motor vehicles – accumulated depreciation		1 Oct	8,090.00			
	Cr	VAT on sales		1 Oct	7,420.60			
	Dr	VAT on purchases		1 Oct	3,930.00			
	Cr	Capital		1 Oct	31,087.25			
	Cr	Bank loan		1 Oct	20,000.00			
	Dr	Sales ledger control *		1 Oct	6,624.90			
	Cr	Purchase ledger control * *If appropriate		1 Oct	4,797.05			
4	Sales inv	SHI001	Sales – Gas fires	2 Oct	13,874.00	2,774.80		
	Sales inv	HOM001	Sales – Gas fires	10 Oct	12,908.00	2,581.60		
	Sales inv	HOM001	Sales – Electric fires	10 Oct	4,600.00	920.00		
	Sales CN	CRA001	Sales – Electric fires	12 Oct	70.00	14.00	✓	
	Sales CN	SHI001	Sales – Gas fires	14 Oct	1,620.00	324.00		
5	Purchase inv	EAS001	Goods	13 Oct	3,740.00	748.00		
	Purchase CN	EAS001	Goods	17 Oct	47.00	9.40	✓	
	Purchase inv	CHR001	Repairs	25 Oct	876.00	175.20		
6	Bank payment	Bank	Vehicle Insurance	16 Oct	1,490.60			✓
	Cr	Bank Current		17 Oct	10,000.00			✓
	Dr	Bank Deposit		17 Oct	10,000.00			
	Bank receipt		Sales – Gas fires	29 Oct	362.00	72.40		
	Bank receipt		Sales – Gas fires	29 Oct	724.00	144.80		
	Bank receipt		Sales – Electric fires	29 Oct	146.00	29.20		
7	Customer receipt	SHI001	Bank	26 Oct	1,670.00		✓	✓
	Customer receipt	CRA001	Bank	26 Oct	4,220.40		✓	✓
	Customer receipt	HOM001	Bank	28 Oct	2,000.00		✓	✓
8	Supplier payment	EAS001	Bank	20 Oct	2,820.10		✓	✓
	Supplier payment	MAR001	Bank	24 Oct	940.55		✓	✓

9	Bank receipt	Bank	Rental Income – DD	1 Oct	600.00	120.00		✔
	Bank payment	Bank	General rates	5 Oct	142.00			✔
10	Cr	Bank		1 Oct	40.00			✔
	Dr	Petty cash		1 Oct	40.00			
	Cash payment	Petty cash	Postage	17 Oct	8.60			
	Cash payment	Petty cash	Stationery	18 Oct	12.00	2.40		
	Cash payment	Petty cash	Stationery	18 Oct	13.75	2.75		
11	Journal debit	Wages		30 Oct	1,000.00			
	Journal credit	Drawings		30 Oct	1,000.00			
	Journal debit	Bank		30 Oct	18.00			✔
	Journal credit	General rates		30 Oct	18.00			
12	Bank payment	Bank	Bank charges	30 Oct	23.60			✔

Evidence 1a – All customer transactions

Date:		Frances Fireplaces		Page: 1

Frances Fireplaces
Customer Activity (Detailed)

Date From:	01/01/1980		Customer From:	
Date To:	31/10/2016		Customer To:	ZZZZZZZZ
Transaction From:	1		N/C From:	
Transaction To:	99,999,999		N/C To:	99999999
Inc b/fwd transaction:	No		Dept From:	0
Exc later payment:	No		Dept To:	999

** NOTE: All report values are shown in Base Currency, unless otherwise indicated **

A/C:	CRA001	Name:	Cranthorne Interiors		Contact:	Habibe Mahmood		Tel:	0162 748542

No	Type	Date	Ref	N/C	Details	Dept	T/C	Value	O/S	Debit	Credit	V	B
1	SI	01/10/2016	O/Bal	9998	Opening Balance	0	T9	4,304.40		4,304.40		-	-
30	SC	12/10/2016	67	4001	Electric fires returned	0	T1	84.00			84.00	N	-
42	SR	26/10/2016	Cheque	1200	Sales Receipt	0	T9	4,220.40			4,220.40	-	R
							Totals:	0.00	0.00	4,304.40	4,304.40		

Amount Outstanding	0.00
Amount Paid this period	4,220.40
Credit Limit £	5,000.00
Turnover YTD	4,234.40

A/C:	HOM001	Name:	Homeware Showroom		Contact:	Claire Hemmingway		Tel:	0162 147526

No	Type	Date	Ref	N/C	Details	Dept	T/C	Value	O/S	Debit	Credit	V	B
2	SI	01/10/2016	O/Bal	9998	Opening Balance	0	T9	650.50 *	650.50	650.50		-	-
28	SI	10/10/2016	281	4000	Gas fires	0	T1	15,489.60 *	15,489.60	15,489.60		N	-
29	SI	10/10/2016	281	4001	Electric fires	0	T1	5,520.00 *	5,520.00	5,520.00		N	-
43	SA	28/10/2016	Cheque	1200	Payment on Account	0	T9	2,000.00 *	-2,000.00		2,000.00	-	N
							Totals:	19,660.10	19,660.10	21,660.10	2,000.00		

Amount Outstanding	19,660.10
Amount Paid this period	2,000.00
Credit Limit £	25,000.00
Turnover YTD	18,158.50

A/C:	SHI001	Name:	Shirley Styles		Contact:	Phillip Sandford		Tel:	0178 264240

No	Type	Date	Ref	N/C	Details	Dept	T/C	Value	O/S	Debit	Credit	V	B
3	SI	01/10/2016	O/Bal	9998	Opening Balance	0	T9	1,670.00		1,670.00		-	-
27	SI	02/10/2016	280	4000	Gas fires	0	T1	16,648.80 *	16,648.80	16,648.80		N	-
31	SC	14/10/2016	68	4000	Gas fires returned	0	T1	1,944.00 *	-1,944.00		1,944.00	N	-
41	SR	26/10/2016	BACS	1200	Sales Receipt	0	T9	1,670.00			1,670.00	-	R
							Totals:	14,704.80	14,704.80	18,318.80	3,614.00		

Amount Outstanding	14,704.80
Amount Paid this period	1,670.00
Credit Limit £	28,000.00
Turnover YTD	13,924.00

Evidence 1b – Balance owed by each customer

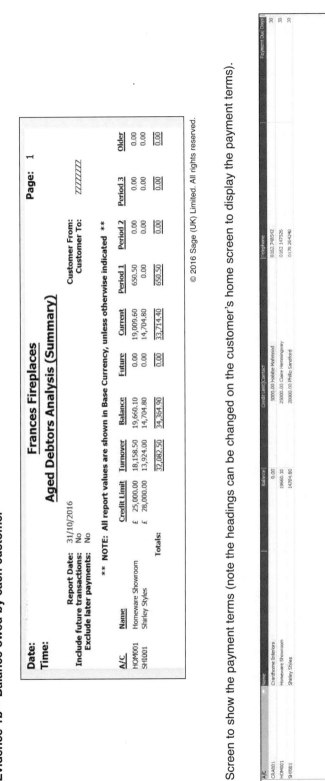

| Date: | | **Frances Fireplaces** | | | | | | Page: 1 |
| Time: | | **Aged Debtors Analysis (Summary)** | | | | | | |

Report Date:	31/10/2016					**Customer From:**		
Include future transactions:	No					**Customer To:**	///////	
Exclude later payments:	No							

** NOTE: All report values are shown in Base Currency, unless otherwise indicated **

A/C	**Name**	**Credit Limit**	**Turnover**	**Balance**	**Future**	**Current**	**Period 1**	**Period 2**	**Period 3**	**Older**
HOM001	Homeware Showroom	£ 25,000.00	18,158.50	19,660.10	0.00	19,009.60	650.50	0.00	0.00	0.00
SHI001	Shirley Styles	£ 28,000.00	13,924.00	14,704.80	0.00	14,704.80	0.00	0.00	0.00	0.00
	Totals:		32,082.50	34,364.90	0.00	33,714.40	650.50	0.00	0.00	0.00

Screen to show the payment terms (note the headings can be changed on the customer's home screen to display the payment terms).

A/C	Name	Balance	Credit Limit	Contact	Telephone	Payment Due Days
CRA001	Cranthorne Interiors	0.00	5000.00	Habibe Mahmood	0162 748542	30
HOM001	Homeware Showroom	19660.10	25000.00	Claire Hemmingway	0162 147526	30
SHI001	Shirley Styles	14704.80	28000.00	Philip Sandford	0176 264240	30

Evidence 2a – All supplier transactions

Date:				**Frances Fireplaces**					Page: 1
Time:				**Supplier Activity (Detailed)**					

Date From:	01/01/1980					Supplier From:	
Date To:	31/10/2016					Supplier To:	ZZZZZZZZ
Transaction From:	1					N/C From:	
Transaction To:	99,999,999					N/C To:	99999999
Inc b/fwd transaction:	No					Dept From:	0
Exc later payment:	No					Dept To:	999

** NOTE: All report values are shown in Base Currency, unless otherwise indicated **

A/C:	CHR001	**Name:**	Chris Carrington Ltd		**Contact:**	Mark Carrington		**Tel:**	0178 364214

No	Type	Date	Ref	N/C	Details	Dept	T/C	Value	O/S	Debit	Credit	V	B
4	PI	01/10/2016	O/Bal	9998	Opening Balance	0	T9	980.00 *	980.00		980.00	-	~
33	PI	25/10/2016	0014582	7800	Repairs to showroom	0	T1	1,051.20 *	1,051.20		1,051.20	N	-
					Totals:			2,031.20	2,031.20	0.00	2,031.20		

Amount Outstanding	2,031.20	
Amount paid this period	0.00	
Credit Limit £	2,500.00	
Turnover YTD	1,856.00	

A/C:	EAS001	**Name:**	East Town Electrics		**Contact:**	Seema Tomlinson		**Tel:**	0191 471256

No	Type	Date	Ref	N/C	Details	Dept	T/C	Value	O/S	Debit	Credit	V	B
5	PI	01/10/2016	O/Bal	9998	Opening Balance	0	T9	2,876.50	0.00		2,876.50	-	-
32	PI	13/10/2016	745526	5000	Supply of goods for resale	0	T1	4,488.00 *	4,488.00		4,488.00	N	~
34	PC	17/10/2016	CN541	5000	Goods for resale returned	0	T1	56.40	0.00	56.40		N	-
44	PP	20/10/2016	020142	1200	Purchase Payment	0	T9	2,820.10	0.00	2,820.10		-	R
					Totals:			4,488.00	4,488.00	2,876.50	7,364.50		

Amount Outstanding	4,488.00	
Amount paid this period	2,820.10	
Credit Limit £	8,000.00	
Turnover YTD	6,569.50	

A/C:	MAR001	**Name:**	Mark Sharpe		**Contact:**	Mark Sharpe		**Tel:**	0162 589301

No	Type	Date	Ref	N/C	Details	Dept	T/C	Value	O/S	Debit	Credit	V	B
6	PI	01/10/2016	O/Bal	9998	Opening Balance	0	T9	940.55	0.00		940.55	-	-
45	PP	24/10/2016	BACS	1200	Purchase Payment	0	T9	940.55	0.00	940.55		-	R
					Totals:			0.00	0.00	940.55	940.55		

Amount Outstanding	0.00	
Amount paid this period	940.55	
Credit Limit £	3,500.00	
Turnover YTD	940.55	

Evidence 2b – Balance owed by suppliers

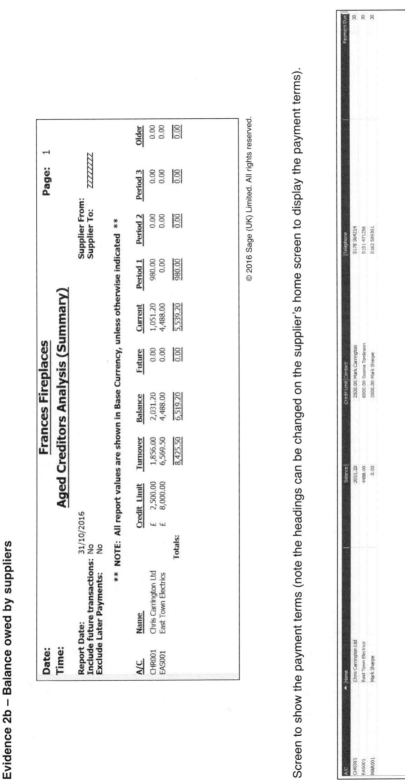

Frances Fireplaces

Aged Creditors Analysis (Summary)

Date:
Time:
Page: 1

Report Date: 31/10/2016
Include future transactions: No
Exclude Later Payments: No

Supplier From:
Supplier To: ZZZZZZZ

** NOTE: All report values are shown in Base Currency, unless otherwise indicated **

A/C	Name	Credit Limit	Turnover	Balance	Future	Current	Period 1	Period 2	Period 3	Older
CHR001	Chris Carrington Ltd	£ 2,500.00	1,856.00	2,031.20	0.00	1,051.20	980.00	0.00	0.00	0.00
EAS001	East Town Electrics	£ 8,000.00	6,569.50	4,488.00	0.00	4,488.00	0.00	0.00	0.00	0.00
	Totals:		8,425.50	6,519.20	0.00	5,539.20	980.00	0.00	0.00	0.00

Screen to show the payment terms (note the headings can be changed on the supplier's home screen to display the payment terms).

A/C	Name	Balance	Credit Limit	Contact	Telephone	Payment Due
CHR001	Chris Carrington Ltd	2031.20	2500.00	Mark Carrington	0178 364214	30
EAS001	East Town Electrics	4488.00	8000.00	Seema Tomlinson	0191 471256	30
MAR001	Mark Sharpe	0.00	3500.00	Mark Sharpe	0162 599301	30

Evidence 3 – An audit trail, showing full details of all transactions, including details of receipts/payments allocated to items in customer/supplier accounts and details of items in the bank account that have been reconciled.

Date:														

Frances Fireplaces
Audit Trail (Detailed)

Page: 1

Date From:	01/01/1980	Customer From:	
Date To:	31/12/2019	Customer To:	ZZZZZZZZ
Transaction From:	1	Supplier From:	
Transaction To:	99,999,999	Supplier To:	ZZZZZZZZ

Exclude Deleted Tran: No

No	Type	A/C	N/C	Dept	Details	Date	Ref	Net	Tax	T/C	Pd	Paid	V	B	Bank Rec.
1	SI	CRA001				01/10/2016	O/Bal	4,304.40	0.00		Y	4,304.40	-		
		1	9998	0	Opening Balance			4,304.40	0.00	T9		4,304.40	-		
					84.00 from SC 30	12/10/2016	67					84.00			
					4220.40 from SR 42	26/10/2016	Cheque					4,220.40			
2	SI	HOM001				01/10/2016	O/Bal	650.50	0.00		N	0.00	-		
		2	9998	0	Opening Balance			650.50	0.00	T9		0.00	-		
3	SI	SHI001				01/10/2016	O/Bal	1,670.00	0.00		Y	1,670.00	-		
		3	9998	0	Opening Balance			1,670.00	0.00	T9		1,670.00	-		
					1670.00 from SR 41	26/10/2016	BACS					1,670.00			
4	PI	CHR001				01/10/2016	O/Bal	980.00	0.00		N	0.00	-		
		4	9998	0	Opening Balance			980.00	0.00	T9		0.00	-		
5	PI	EAS001				01/10/2016	O/Bal	2,876.50	0.00		Y	2,876.50	-		
		5	9998	0	Opening Balance			2,876.50	0.00	T9		2,876.50	-		
					56.40 from PC 34	17/10/2016	CN541					56.40			
					2820.10 from PP 44	20/10/2016	020142					2,820.10			
6	PI	MAR001				01/10/2016	O/Bal	940.55	0.00		Y	940.55	-		
		6	9998	0	Opening Balance			940.55	0.00	T9		940.55	-		
					940.55 from PP 45	24/10/2016	BACS					940.55			
7	JD	1200				01/10/2016	O/Bal	16,000.00	0.00		Y	16,000.00	-		01/10/2016
		7	1200	0	Opening Balance			16,000.00	0.00	T9		16,000.00	-		
8	JC	9998				01/10/2016	O/Bal	16,000.00	0.00		Y	16,000.00	-		
		8	9998	0	Opening Balance			16,000.00	0.00	T9		16,000.00	-		
9	JD	1230				01/10/2016	O/Bal	160.00	0.00		Y	160.00	-		01/10/2016
		9	1230	0	Opening Balance			160.00	0.00	T9		160.00	-		
10	JC	9998				01/10/2016	O/Bal	160.00	0.00		Y	160.00	-		
		10	9998	0	Opening Balance			160.00	0.00	T9		160.00	-		
11	JD	0030				01/10/2016	O/Bal	15,400.00	0.00		Y	15,400.00	-		
		11	0030	0	Opening Balance			15,400.00	0.00	T9		15,400.00	-		
12	JC	9998				01/10/2016	O/Bal	15,400.00	0.00		Y	15,400.00	-		
		12	9998	0	Opening Balance			15,400.00	0.00	T9		15,400.00	-		
13	JC	0031				01/10/2016	O/Bal	3,080.00	0.00		Y	3,080.00	-		
		13	0031	0	Opening Balance			3,080.00	0.00	T9		3,080.00	-		
14	JD	9998				01/10/2016	O/Bal	3,080.00	0.00		Y	3,080.00	-		
		14	9998	0	Opening Balance			3,080.00	0.00	T9		3,080.00	-		
15	JD	0050				01/10/2016	O/Bal	32,360.00	0.00		Y	32,360.00	-		
		15	0050	0	Opening Balance			32,360.00	0.00	T9		32,360.00	-		
16	JC	9998				01/10/2016	O/Bal	32,360.00	0.00		Y	32,360.00	-		
		16	9998	0	Opening Balance			32,360.00	0.00	T9		32,360.00	-		
17	JC	0051				01/10/2016	O/Bal	8,090.00	0.00		Y	8,090.00	-		
		17	0051	0	Opening Balance			8,090.00	0.00	T9		8,090.00	-		
18	JD	9998				01/10/2016	O/Bal	8,090.00	0.00		Y	8,090.00	-		
		18	9998	0	Opening Balance			8,090.00	0.00	T9		8,090.00	-		
19	JC	2200				01/10/2016	O/Bal	7,420.60	0.00		Y	7,420.60	-		
		19	2200	0	Opening Balance			7,420.60	0.00	T9		7,420.60	-		
20	JD	9998				01/10/2016	O/Bal	7,420.60	0.00		Y	7,420.60	-		
		20	9998	0	Opening Balance			7,420.60	0.00	T9		7,420.60	-		
21	JD	2201				01/10/2016	O/Bal	3,930.00	0.00		Y	3,930.00	-		
		21	2201	0	Opening Balance			3,930.00	0.00	T9		3,930.00	-		
22	JC	9998				01/10/2016	O/Bal	3,930.00	0.00		Y	3,930.00	-		
		22	9998	0	Opening Balance			3,930.00	0.00	T9		3,930.00	-		
23	JC	3000				01/10/2016	O/Bal	31,087.25	0.00		Y	31,087.25	-		
		23	3000	0	Opening Balance			31,087.25	0.00	T9		31,087.25	-		
24	JD	9998				01/10/2016	O/Bal	31,087.25	0.00		Y	31,087.25	-		
		24	9998	0	Opening Balance			31,087.25	0.00	T9		31,087.25	-		
25	JC	2300				01/10/2016	O/Bal	20,000.00	0.00		Y	20,000.00	-		
		25	2300	0	Opening Balance			20,000.00	0.00	T9		20,000.00	-		
26	JD	9998				01/10/2016	O/Bal	20,000.00	0.00		Y	20,000.00	-		
		26	9998	0	Opening Balance			20,000.00	0.00	T9		20,000.00	-		
27	SI	SHI001				02/10/2016	280	13,874.00	2,774.80		N	0.00			
		27	4000	0	Gas fires			13,874.00	2,774.80	T1		0.00	N		

No	Type	A/C	Line	N/C	Dept	Details	Date	Ref	Net	Tax	T	Paid	Amount	R	Bank Date
28	SI	HOM001					10/10/2016	281	17,508.00	3,501.60		N	0.00	-	
			28	4000	0	Gas fires			12,908.00	2,501.60	T1		0.00	N	
			29	4001	0	Electric fires			4,600.00	920.00	T1		0.00	N	
30	SC	CRA001					12/10/2016	67	70.00	14.00		Y	84.00	-	
			30	4001	0	Electric fires returned			70.00	14.00	T1		84.00	N	
						84.00 to SI 1	12/10/2016	O/Bal					84.00		
31	SC	SHI001					14/10/2016	68	1,620.00	324.00		N	0.00	-	
			31	4000	0	Gas fires returned			1,620.00	324.00	T1		0.00	N	
32	PI	EAS001					13/10/2016	745526	3,740.00	748.00		N	0.00	-	
			32	5000	0	Supply of goods for resale			3,740.00	748.00	T1		0.00	N	
33	PI	CHR001					25/10/2016	0014582	876.00	175.20		N	0.00	-	
			33	7800	0	Repairs to showroom			876.00	175.20	T1		0.00	N	
34	PC	EAS001					17/10/2016	CN541	47.00	9.40		Y	56.40	-	
			34	5000	0	Goods for resale returned			47.00	9.40	T1		56.40	N	
						56.40 to PI 5	17/10/2016	O/Bal					56.40		
35	BP	1200					16/10/2016	Debit card	1,490.60	0.00		Y	1,490.60	R	31/10/2016
			35	7303	0	Vehicle Insurance			1,490.60	0.00	T2		1,490.60	N	
36	JC	1200					17/10/2016	TRANS	10,000.00	0.00		Y	10,000.00	R	31/10/2016
			36	1200	0	Bank Transfer			10,000.00	0.00	T9		10,000.00	-	
37	JD	1210					17/10/2016	TRANS	10,000.00	0.00		Y	10,000.00	N	
			37	1210	0	Bank Transfer			10,000.00	0.00	T9		10,000.00	-	
38	BR	1200					29/10/2016	56	362.00	72.40		Y	434.40	N	
			38	4000	0	x2 gas fires			362.00	72.40	T1		434.40	N	
39	BR	1200					29/10/2016	57	870.00	174.00		Y	1,044.00	N	
			39	4000	0	x4 gas fires			724.00	144.80	T1		868.80	N	
			40	4001	0	x1 electric fire			146.00	29.20	T1		175.20	N	
41	SR	SHI001					26/10/2016	BACS	1,670.00	0.00		Y	1,670.00	R	31/10/2016
			41	1200	0	Sales Receipt			1,670.00	0.00	T9		1,670.00	-	
						1670.00 to SI 3	26/10/2016	O/Bal					1,670.00		
42	SR	CRA001					26/10/2016	Cheque	4,220.40	0.00		Y	4,220.40	R	31/10/2016
			42	1200	0	Sales Receipt			4,220.40	0.00	T9		4,220.40	-	
						4220.40 to SI 1	26/10/2016	O/Bal					4,220.40		
43	SA	HOM001					28/10/2016	Cheque	2,000.00	0.00		N	0.00	N	
			43	1200	0	Payment on Account			2,000.00	0.00	T9		0.00		
44	PP	EAS001					20/10/2016	020142	2,820.10	0.00		Y	2,820.10	R	31/10/2016
			44	1200	0	Purchase Payment			2,820.10	0.00	T9		2,820.10	-	
						2820.10 to PI 5	20/10/2016	O/Bal					2,820.10		
45	PP	MAR001					24/10/2016	BACS	940.55	0.00		Y	940.55	R	31/10/2016
			45	1200	0	Purchase Payment			940.55	0.00	T9		940.55	-	
						940.55 to PI 6	24/10/2016	O/Bal					940.55		
46	BR	1200					01/10/2016	STO	600.00	120.00		Y	720.00	R	31/10/2016
			46	4904	0	S Shaw rental income			600.00	120.00	T1		720.00	N	
47	BP	1200					05/10/2016	STO	142.00	0.00		Y	142.00	R	31/10/2016
			47	7103	0	Gilford council rates			142.00	0.00	T2		142.00	N	
48	JC	1200					01/10/2016	TRANS	40.00	0.00		Y	40.00	R	31/10/2016
			48	1200	0	Bank Transfer			40.00	0.00	T9		40.00	-	
49	JD	1230					01/10/2016	TRANS	40.00	0.00		Y	40.00	-	
			49	1230	0	Bank Transfer			40.00	0.00	T9		40.00	-	
50	CP	1230					17/10/2016	101	8.60	0.00		Y	8.60	-	
			50	7501	0	Postage stamps			8.60	0.00	T2		8.60	N	
51	CP	1230					18/10/2016	102	12.00	2.40		Y	14.40	-	
			51	7502	0	Envelopes			12.00	2.40	T1		14.40	N	
52	CP	1230					18/10/2016	103	13.75	2.75		Y	16.50	-	
			52	7502	0	Ink for printer			13.75	2.75	T1		16.50	N	
53	JD	7000					30/10/2016	061	1,000.00	0.00		Y	1,000.00	-	
			53	7000	0	Wages incorrectly posted			1,000.00	0.00	T9		1,000.00	-	
54	JC	3050					30/10/2016	061	1,000.00	0.00		Y	1,000.00	-	
			54	3050	0	Wages incorrectly posted			1,000.00	0.00	T9		1,000.00	-	
55	JD	1200					30/10/2016	062	18.00	0.00		Y	18.00	R	31/10/2016
			55	1200	0	Error in standing order			18.00	0.00	T9		18.00	-	
56	JC	7103					30/10/2016	062	18.00	0.00		Y	18.00	-	
			56	7103	0	Error in standing order			18.00	0.00	T9		18.00	-	
57	BP	1200					30/10/2016		23.60	0.00		Y	23.60	R	31/10/2016
			57	7901	0	Charges incurred			23.60	0.00	T2		23.60	N	

Evidence 4 – Trial balance as at 31 October 20-X

Date:		Frances Fireplaces	Page: 1
Time:		**Period Trial Balance**	

To Period: Month 12, October 2017

N/C	Name	Debit	Credit
0030	Office Equipment	15,400.00	
0031	Office Equipment Depreciation		3,080.00
0050	Motor Vehicles	32,360.00	
0051	Motor Vehicles Depreciation		8,090.00
1100	Debtors Control Account	34,364.90	
1200	Bank Current Account	10,649.95	
1210	Bank Deposit Account	10,000.00	
1230	Petty Cash	160.50	
2100	Creditors Control Account		6,519.20
2200	Sales Tax Control Account		13,725.40
2201	Purchase Tax Control Account	4,848.95	
2300	Loans		20,000.00
3000	Capital		31,087.25
3050	Drawings		1,000.00
4000	Sales - Gas fires		26,248.00
4001	Sales - Electric fires		4,676.00
4904	Rent Income		600.00
5000	Materials Purchased	3,693.00	
7000	Gross Wages	1,000.00	
7103	General Rates	124.00	
7303	Vehicle Insurance	1,490.60	
7501	Postage and Carriage	8.60	
7502	Office Stationery	25.75	
7800	Repairs and Renewals	876.00	
7901	Bank Charges	23.60	
	Totals:	115,025.85	115,025.85

Evidence 5a – Screenshot of the rocurring entry set up screen, including all relevant input detail.

Evidence 5b – Screenshot of the recurring entry set up screen, including all relevant input detail.

Add / Edit Recurring Entry

Recurring Entry From / To

Bank A/C*	1200	Bank Current Account
Nominal Code*	7103	General Rates

Recurring Entry Details

Transaction Type	Bank/Cash/Credit Card Payment
Transaction Ref	STO
Transaction Details	Gilford council rates
Department*	0	Default

Posting Frequency

Every*	1	Month(s)	Total Required Postings: 12
Start Date*	05/10/2016		Finish Date: 05/09/2017
Next Posting Date	05/10/2016		Suspend Posting ?
Last Posted			

Posting Amounts

Net Amount: 142.00   Tax Code* T2 0.00   VAT: 0.00

OK   Cancel

Add / Edit Recurring Entry

Recurring Entry From / To

Bank A/C To*	1200	Bank Current Account
Nominal Code*	4904	Rent Income

Recurring Entry Details

Transaction Type	Bank/Cash/Credit Card Receipt
Transaction Ref	STO
Transaction Details	S Shaw rental income
Department*	0	Default

Posting Frequency

Every*	1	Month(s)	Total Required Postings: 6
Start Date*	01/10/2016		Finish Date: 01/03/2017
Next Posting Date	01/10/2016		Suspend Posting ?
Last Posted			

Posting Amounts

Net Amount: 600.00   Tax Code* T1 20.00   VAT: 120.00

OK   Cancel

Evidence 6 – Bank reconciliation transactions (the associated screenshot is on the next page).

Date:
Time:

Frances Fireplaces
Bank Reconciled Transactions

Page: 1

Bank Reconciled On: 01/10/2016

No	Type	Date	A/C	N/C	Dept	Ref	Details	Net	Tax	T/C
7	JD	01/10/2016	1200	1200	0	O/Bal	Opening Balance	16,000.00	0.00	T9

Bank Reconciled On: 31/10/2016

No	Type	Date	A/C	N/C	Dept	Ref	Details	Net	Tax	T/C
35	BP	16/10/2016	1200	7303	0	Debit card	Vehicle Insurance	1,490.60	0.00	T2
36	JC	17/10/2016	1200	1200	0	TRANS	Bank Transfer	10,000.00	0.00	T9
41	SR	26/10/2016	SHI001	1200	0	BACS	Sales Receipt	1,670.00	0.00	T9
42	SR	26/10/2016	CRA001	1200	0	Cheque	Sales Receipt	4,220.40	0.00	T9
44	PP	20/10/2016	EAS001	1200	0	020142	Purchase Payment	2,820.10	0.00	T9
45	PP	24/10/2016	MAR001	1200	0	BACS	Purchase Payment	940.55	0.00	T9
46	BR	01/10/2016	1200	4904	0	STO	S Shaw rental income	600.00	120.00	T1
47	BP	05/10/2016	1200	7103	0	STO	Gilford council rates	142.00	0.00	T2
48	JC	01/10/2016	1200	1200	0	TRANS	Bank Transfer	40.00	0.00	T9
55	JD	30/10/2016	1200	1200	0	062	Error in standing order	18.00	0.00	T9
57	BP	30/10/2016	1200	7901	0		Charges incurred	23.60	0.00	T2

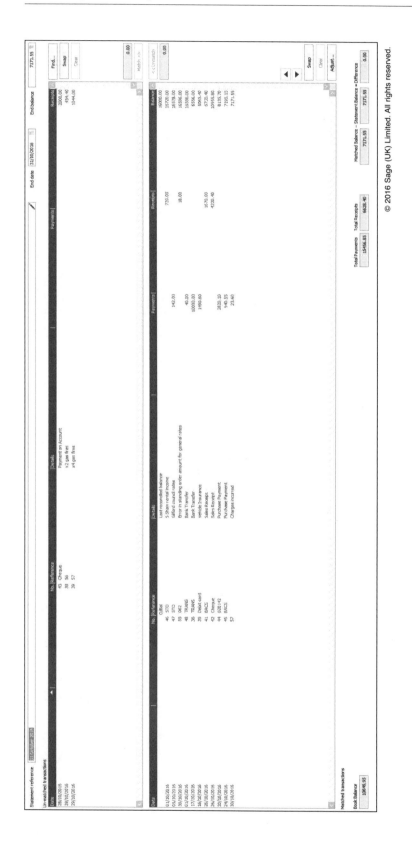

Statement reference: | End date 31/10/2016 | End balance 7171.55

Un-matched transactions

Date	No.	Reference	Details	Payments	Receipts
28/10/2016	43	Cheque	Payment on Account		3000.00
29/10/2016	33	56	x2 gas fires		494.40
29/10/2016	39	57	x4 gas fires		1044.00

Find... | Swap | Clear | 0.00

Match >> | << Unmatch | 0.00

Date	No.	Reference	Details	Payments	Receipts	Balance
01/10/2016		O.Bal	Last reconciled balance			16000.00
01/10/2016	46	STD	S Shaw rental income		720.00	15720.00
05/10/2016	47	STD	Gifford council rates	142.00		15578.00
30/10/2016	55	062	Error in standing order amount for general rates		18.00	15596.00
01/10/2016	48	TRANS	Bank Transfer	40.00		15556.00
17/10/2016	36	TRANS	Bank Transfer	10093.00		6596.00
16/10/2016	35	Debit card	vehicle Insurance	1490.60		5065.40
26/10/2016	41	BACS	Sales Receipt		1670.00	6735.40
26/10/2016	42	Cheque	Sales Receipt		4230.40	10955.80
20/10/2016	44	0261 HQ	Purchase Payment	2820.10		8155.70
24/10/2016	45	BACS	Purchase Payment	940.55		7355.15
30/10/2016	57		Charges incurred	23.63		7171.55

Total Payments 15496.85 | Total Receipts 6628.40 | Matched Balance - Statement Balance = Difference 7171.55

Matched transactions

Book Balance 10646.95

Swap | Clear | Adjust...

Matched Balance 7171.55 | Statement Balance 7171.55 | Difference 0.00

Answers to
practice
assessment 2

Task	Transaction Type	Account(s)		Date 20-X	Net Amount £	VAT £	Allocated against receipt/ payment ✓	Reconciled with bank statement ✓
1	Customer O/bal	BIN001		1 Mar	12,404.40		✓	
	Customer O/bal	LIM001		1 Mar	1,605.95		✓	
	Customer O/bal	TOW001		1 Mar	3,480.00			
2	Supplier O/bal	ARN001		1 Mar	976.20			
	Supplier O/bal	CAM001		1 Mar	4,900.50		✓	
	Supplier O/bal	WAL001		1 Mar	7,500.60			
3	Cr	Bank current account		1 Mar	3,460.00			✓
	Dr	Petty cash		1 Mar	200.00			
	Dr	Plant and machinery - cost		1 Mar	25,600.00			
	Cr	Plant and machinery – accumulated depreciation		1 Mar	12,800.00			
				1 Mar				
	Dr	Furniture - cost		1 Mar	32,802.00			
	Cr	Furniture - accumulated depreciation		1 Mar	9,840.60			
				1 Mar				
	Dr	Motor vehicles - cost		1 Mar	26,882.08			
	Cr	Motor vehicles - accumulated depreciation		1 Mar	10,752.83			
				1 Mar				
	Cr	VAT on sales		1 Mar	9,800.00			
	Dr	VAT on purchases		1 Mar	5,607.00			
	Cr	Capital		1 Mar	48,550.70			
	Dr	Sales ledger control *		1 Mar	17,490.35			
	Cr	Purchase ledger control * *If appropriate		1 Mar	13,377.30			
4	Sales inv	TOW001	Sales – Decorating services	3 Mar	15,780.00	3,156.00		
			Decorating supplies		2,010.00	402.00		
	Sales inv	LIM001	Sales – Decorating services	4 Mar	800.00	160.00	✓	
			Decorating supplies		607.00	121.40	✓	
	Sales inv	BIN001	Sales – Decorating services	20 Mar	7,093.10	1,418.62		
	Sales CN	LIM001	Sales - Decorating supplies	5 Mar	81.00	16.20	✓	
	Sales CN	TOW001	Sales - Decorating supplies	23 Mar	4,000.00	800.00		

5	Purchase inv	WAL001	Purchases – Wallpaper	2 Mar	1,250.00	250.00	✓	
			Decorating		310.00	62.00	✓	
	Purchase inv	CAM001	Purchases – Wallpaper	5 Mar	2,620.84	524.17	✓	
			Decorating		641.00	128.20	✓	
	Purchase inv	ARN001	Purchases – Wallpaper	7 Mar	1,021.00	204.20		
			Decorating		54.80	10.96		
	Purchase CN	WAL001	Purchase returns – Wallpaper	14 Mar	20.00	4.00		
			Decorating		92.32	18.46		
	Purchase CN	ARN001	Purchase returns – Wallpaper	18 Mar	31.68	6.34		
6	Bank payment	Bank	Drawings	21 Mar	175.00			✓
	Bank payment	Bank	Wages	30 Mar	4,980.00			✓
	Bank receipt		Sales – Decorating supplies	13 Mar	432.50	86.50		✓
7	Customer receipt	BIN001	Bank	2 Mar	12,404.40		✓	✓
	Customer receipt	LIM001	Bank	10 Mar	1,591.20		✓	✓
	Customer receipt	LIM001	Bank	24 Mar	1,605.95		✓	✓
	Customer receipt	TOW001	Bank	27 Mar	5,000.00			✓
8	Supplier payment	ARN001	Bank	20 Mar	1,500.00			✓
	Supplier payment	WAL001	Bank	22 Mar	1,737.22		✓	✓
	Supplier payment	CAM001	Bank	23 Mar	4,900.50		✓	✓
9	Bank payment	Bank	Telephone – DD	18 Mar	84.00	16.80		✓
	Bank payment	Bank	Equipment leasing - STO	20 Mar	106.00	21.20		✓
10	Cr	Bank		1 Mar	50.00			✓
	Dr	Petty cash		1 Mar	50.00			
	Cash payment	Petty cash	Stationery	3 Mar	4.67	0.93		
	Cash payment	Petty cash	Cleaning	9 Mar	6.20	1.24		
	Cash payment	Petty cash	Postage	15 Mar	7.50			
	Cash payment	Petty cash	Postage	23 Mar	21.00			
11	Journal debit	Sales – Decorating supplies		30 Mar	46.00			
	Journal credit	Sales – Decorating services		30 Mar	46.00			
12	Bank payment	Bank	Bank charges	31 Mar	18.00			✓
	Bank payment	Bank	General rates	26 Mar	130.00			✓

Evidence 1a – All customer transactions

Date:					
Time:		**Dolby Decorating**		**Page:**	1
		Customer Activity (Detailed)			

Date From:	01/01/1980	**Customer From:**	
Date To:	31/03/2016	**Customer To:**	ZZZZZZZZ
Transaction From:	1	**N/C From:**	
Transaction To:	99,999,999	**N/C To:**	99999999
Inc b/fwd transaction:	No	**Dept From:**	0
Exc later payment:	No	**Dept To:**	999

** NOTE: All report values are shown in Base Currency, unless otherwise indicated **

A/C: BIN001 **Name:** Bingham Housing **Contact:** Sanjay Sarma **Tel:** 0196 745240

No	Type	Date	Ref	N/C	Details	Dept	T/C	Value	O/S	Debit	Credit	V	B
1	SI	01/03/2016	O/Bal	9998	Opening Balance	0	T9	12,404.40		12,404.40		-	-
33	SI	20/03/2016	BIN001/IN3	4000	Decorating services	0	T1	8,511.72 *	8,511.72	8,511.72		N	-
48	SR	02/03/2016	BACS	1200	Sales Receipt	0	T9	12,404.40			12,404.40	-	R
							Totals:	8,511.72	8,511.72	20,916.12	12,404.40		

Amount Outstanding	8,511.72
Amount Paid this period	12,404.40
Credit Limit £	23,500.00
Turnover YTD	19,497.50

A/C: LIM001 **Name:** Limegate Decorating Stores **Contact:** Hannah McPhilbin **Tel:** 0180 360214

No	Type	Date	Ref	N/C	Details	Dept	T/C	Value	O/S	Debit	Credit	V	B
2	SI	01/03/2016	O/Bal	9998	Opening Balance	0	T9	1,605.95		1,605.95		-	-
31	SI	04/03/2016	LIM001/IN3	4000	Decorating services	0	T1	960.00		960.00		N	-
32	SI	04/03/2016	LIM001/IN3	4001	Decorating supplies	0	T1	728.40		728.40		N	-
34	SC	05/03/2016	LIM001/C12	4001	Decorating supplies returned	0	T1	97.20			97.20	N	-
49	SR	10/03/2016	BACS	1200	Sales Receipt	0	T9	1,591.20			1,591.20	-	R
50	SR	24/03/2016	BACS	1200	Sales Receipt	0	T9	1,605.95			1,605.95	-	R
							Totals:	0.00	0.00	3,294.35	3,294.35		

Amount Outstanding	0.00
Amount Paid this period	3,197.15
Credit Limit £	4,000.00
Turnover YTD	2,931.95

A/C: TOW001 **Name:** Town View Property Services **Contact:** Mary Przada **Tel:** 0180 240240

No	Type	Date	Ref	N/C	Details	Dept	T/C	Value	O/S	Debit	Credit	V	B
3	SI	01/03/2016	O/Bal	9998	Opening Balance	0	T9	3,480.00 *	3,480.00	3,480.00		-	-
29	SI	03/03/2016	TOW001/IN	4000	Decorating services	0	T1	18,936.00 *	18,936.00	18,936.00		N	-
30	SI	03/03/2016	TOW001/IN	4001	Decorating supplies	0	T1	2,412.00 *	2,412.00	2,412.00		N	-
35	SC	23/03/2016	TOW001/C1	4001	Decorating supplies returned	0	T1	4,800.00 *	-4,800.00		4,800.00	N	-
51	SA	27/03/2016	Cheque	1200	Payment on Account	0	T9	5,000.00 *	-5,000.00		5,000.00	-	N
							Totals:	15,028.00	15,028.00	24,828.00	9,800.00		

Amount Outstanding	15,028.00
Amount Paid this period	5,000.00
Credit Limit £	26,000.00
Turnover YTD	17,270.00

Evidence 1b – Balance owed by each customer

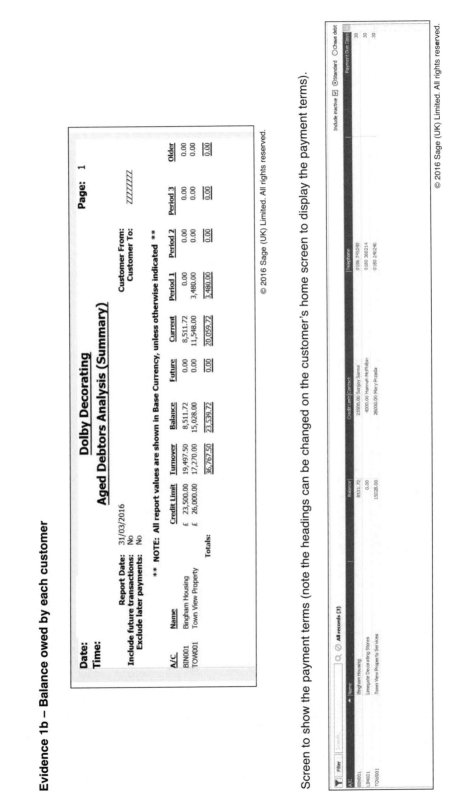

Date:
Time:

Dolby Decorating
Aged Debtors Analysis (Summary)

Page: 1

Report Date: 31/03/2016
Include future transactions: No
Exclude later payments: No

Customer From:
Customer To: ZZZZZZZ

** NOTE: All report values are shown in Base Currency, unless otherwise indicated **

A/C	Name	Credit Limit	Turnover	Balance	Future	Current	Period 1	Period 2	Period 3	Older
BIN001	Bingham Housing	£ 23,500.00	19,497.50	8,511.72	0.00	8,511.72	0.00	0.00	0.00	0.00
TOW001	Town View Property	£ 26,000.00	17,270.00	15,028.00	0.00	11,548.00	3,480.00	0.00	0.00	0.00
	Totals:		36,767.50	23,539.72	0.00	20,059.72	3,480.00	0.00	0.00	0.00

Screen to show the payment terms (note the headings can be changed on the customer's home screen to display the payment terms).

Filter	Search				Include inactive ☑	⊙Standard ○Chase debt
Q ⊘ All records (3)						
A/C	Name	Balance	Credit Limit	Contact	Telephone	Payment Due Days
BIN001	Bingham Housing	8,511.72	23500.00	Sanjay Sarma	0196 745240	30
LIM001	Limejuice Decorating Stores	0.00	4000.00	Hannah McMillan	0180 360214	30
TOW001	Town View Property Services	15028.00	26000.00	Mary Pravda	0180 240240	30

Evidence 2a – All supplier transactions

Date:					**Dolby Decorating**				Page:	1
Time:					**Supplier Activity (Detailed)**					

Date From:	01/01/1980						**Supplier From:**		
Date To:	31/03/2016						**Supplier To:**	ZZZZZZZZ	
Transaction From:	1						**N/C From:**		
Transaction To:	99,999,999						**N/C To:**	99999999	
Inc b/fwd transaction:	No						**Dept From:**	0	
Exc later payment:	No						**Dept To:**	999	

** NOTE: All report values are shown in Base Currency, unless otherwise indicated **

A/C: ARN001 **Name:** Arnold Decorating Warehouse Ltd **Contact:** Hollie Simpson **Tel:** 0131 667778

No	Type	Date	Ref	N/C	Details	Dept	T/C	Value	O/S	Debit	Credit	V	B
4	PI	01/03/2016	O/Bal	9998	Opening Balance	0	T9	976.20 *	976.20		976.20	-	-
40	PI	07/03/2016	PI 419	5000	Wallpaper	0	T1	1,225.20 *	1,225.20		1,225.20	N	-
41	PI	07/03/2016	PI 419	5001	Decorating supplies	0	T1	65.76 *	65.76		65.76	N	-
44	PC	18/03/2016	84	5000	Wallpaper returned	0	T1	38.02 *	-38.02	38.02		N	-
52	PA	20/03/2016	020784	1200	Payment on Account	0	T9	1,500.00 *	-1,500.00	1,500.00		-	R
					Totals:			729.14	729.14	1,538.02	2,267.16		

Amount Outstanding	729.14
Amount paid this period	1,500.00
Credit Limit £	3,000.00
Turnover YTD	2,020.32

A/C: CAM001 **Name:** Campbell & Son Warehouse Ltd **Contact:** John Campbell **Tel:** 0180 200300

No	Type	Date	Ref	N/C	Details	Dept	T/C	Value	O/S	Debit	Credit	V	B
5	PI	01/03/2016	O/Bal	9998	Opening Balance	0	T9	4,900.50	0.00		4,900.50	-	-
38	PI	05/03/2016	D03024	5000	Wallpaper	0	T1	3,145.00 *	3,145.01		3,145.01	N	-
39	PI	05/03/2016	D03024	5001	Decorating supplies	0	T1	769.20 *	769.20		769.20	N	-
54	PP	23/03/2016	020785	1200	Purchase Payment	0	T9	4,900.50	0.00	4,900.50		-	R
					Totals:			3,914.21	3,914.21	4,900.50	8,814.71		

Amount Outstanding	3,914.21
Amount paid this period	4,900.50
Credit Limit £	10,000.00
Turnover YTD	8,162.34

A/C: WAL001 **Name:** Walker Wallpaper Supplies **Contact:** Matt Walker **Tel:** 0117 672954

No	Type	Date	Ref	N/C	Details	Dept	T/C	Value	O/S	Debit	Credit	V	B
6	PI	01/03/2016	O/Bal	9998	Opening Balance	0	T9	7,500.60 *	7,500.60		7,500.60	-	-
36	PI	02/03/2016	INV2978	5000	Wallpaper	0	T1	1,500.00	0.00		1,500.00	N	-
37	PI	02/03/2016	INV2978	5001	Decorating supplies	0	T1	372.00	0.00		372.00	N	-
42	PC	14/03/2016	CN622	5000	Wallpaper returned	0	T1	24.00	0.00	24.00		N	-
43	PC	14/03/2016	CN622	5001	Decorating supplies returned	0	T1	110.78	0.00	110.78		N	-
53	PP	22/03/2016	BACS	1200	Purchase Payment	0	T9	1,737.22	0.00	1,737.22		-	R
					Totals:			7,500.60	7,500.60	1,872.00	9,372.60		

Amount Outstanding	7,500.60
Amount paid this period	1,737.22
Credit Limit £	10,000.00
Turnover YTD	8,948.28

Evidence 2b – Balance owed by suppliers

Dolby Decorating

Aged Creditors Analysis (Summary)

| Date: | | | | | | | | Page: | 1 |

Time:

Report Date: 31/03/2016
Include future transactions: No   Supplier From:
Exclude Later Payments: No   Supplier To: ZZZZZZZZ

** **NOTE: All report values are shown in Base Currency, unless otherwise indicated** **

A/C	Name	Credit Limit	Turnover	Balance	Future	Current	Period 1	Period 2	Period 3	Older
ARN001	Arnold Decorating Warehouse	£ 3,000.00	2,020.32	729.14	0.00	-247.06	976.20	0.00	0.00	0.00
CAM001	Campbell & Son Warehouse	£ 10,000.00	8,162.34	3,914.21	0.00	3,914.21	0.00	0.00	0.00	0.00
WAL001	Walker Wallpaper Supplies	£ 10,000.00	8,948.28	7,500.60	0.00	0.00	7,500.60	0.00	0.00	0.00
	Totals:		19,130.94	12,143.95	0.00	3,667.15	8,476.80	0.00	0.00	0.00

A/C	Name	Balance	Credit Limit	Contact	Telephone	Payment Due
ARN001	Arnold Decorating Warehouse Ltd	729.14	3000.00	Hollie Simpson	0131 667778	30
CAM001	Campbell & Son Warehouse Ltd	3914.21	10000.00	John Campbell	0180 200300	30
WAL001	Walker Wallpaper Supplies	7900.60	10000.00	Matt Walker	0117 672954	30

Evidence 3a – An audit trail, showing full details of all transactions, including details of receipts/payments allocated to items in customer/supplier accounts and details of items in the bank account that have been reconciled.

Date:						**Dolby Decorating**								**Page:** 1	
Time:						**Audit Trail (Detailed)**									

Date From:	01/01/1980		Customer From:	
Date To:	31/12/2019		Customer To:	ZZZZZZZZ
Transaction From:	1		Supplier From:	
Transaction To:	99,999,999		Supplier To:	ZZZZZZZZ

Exclude Deleted Tran: No

No	Type	A/C	N/C	Dept	Details	Date	Ref	Net	Tax	T/C	Pd	Paid	V	B	Bank Rec.
1	SI	BIN001				01/03/2016	O/Bal	12,404.40	0.00		Y	12,404.40	-		
		1	9998	0	Opening Balance			12,404.40	0.00	T9		12,404.40	-		
					12404.40 from SR 48	02/03/2016	BACS					12,404.40			
2	SI	LIM001				01/03/2016	O/Bal	1,605.95	0.00		Y	1,605.95	-		
		2	9998	0	Opening Balance			1,605.95	0.00	T9		1,605.95	-		
					1605.95 from SR 50	24/03/2016	BACS					1,605.95			
3	SI	TOW001				01/03/2016	O/Bal	3,480.00	0.00		N	0.00			
		3	9998	0	Opening Balance			3,480.00	0.00	T9		0.00	-		
4	PI	ARN001				01/03/2016	O/Bal	976.20	0.00		N	0.00			
		4	9998	0	Opening Balance			976.20	0.00	T9		0.00	-		
5	PI	CAM001				01/03/2016	O/Bal	4,900.50	0.00		Y	4,900.50			
		5	9998	0	Opening Balance			4,900.50	0.00	T9		4,900.50	-		
					4900.50 from PP 54	23/03/2016	020785					4,900.50			
6	PI	WAL001				01/03/2016	O/Bal	7,500.60	0.00		N	0.00			
		6	9998	0	Opening Balance			7,500.60	0.00	T9		0.00	-		
7	JC	1200				01/03/2016	O/Bal	3,460.00	0.00		Y	3,460.00	-		01/03/2016
		7	1200	0	Opening Balance			3,460.00	0.00	T9		3,460.00	-		
8	JD	9998				01/03/2016	O/Bal	3,460.00	0.00		Y	3,460.00	-		
		8	9998	0	Opening Balance			3,460.00	0.00	T9		3,460.00	-		
9	JD	1230				01/03/2016	O/Bal	200.00	0.00		Y	200.00	-		01/03/2016
		9	1230	0	Opening Balance			200.00	0.00	T9		200.00	-		
10	JC	9998				01/03/2016	O/Bal	200.00	0.00		Y	200.00			
		10	9998	0	Opening Balance			200.00	0.00	T9		200.00	-		
11	JD	0020				01/03/2016	O/Bal	25,600.00	0.00		Y	25,600.00			
		11	0020	0	Opening Balance			25,600.00	0.00	T9		25,600.00	-		
12	JC	9998				01/03/2016	O/Bal	25,600.00	0.00		Y	25,600.00			
		12	9998	0	Opening Balance			25,600.00	0.00	T9		25,600.00	-		
13	JC	0021				01/03/2016	O/Bal	12,800.00	0.00		Y	12,800.00			
		13	0021	0	Opening Balance			12,800.00	0.00	T9		12,800.00	-		
14	JD	9998				01/03/2016	O/Bal	12,800.00	0.00		Y	12,800.00			
		14	9998	0	Opening Balance			12,800.00	0.00	T9		12,800.00	-		
15	JD	0040				01/03/2016	O/Bal	32,802.00	0.00		Y	32,802.00			
		15	0040	0	Opening Balance			32,802.00	0.00	T9		32,802.00	-		
16	JC	9998				01/03/2016	O/Bal	32,802.00	0.00		Y	32,802.00	-		
		16	9998	0	Opening Balance			32,802.00	0.00	T9		32,802.00	-		
17	JC	0041				01/03/2016	O/Bal	9,840.60	0.00		Y	9,840.60			
		17	0041	0	Opening Balance			9,840.60	0.00	T9		9,840.60	-		
18	JD	9998				01/03/2016	O/Bal	9,840.60	0.00		Y	9,840.60			
		18	9998	0	Opening Balance			9,840.60	0.00	T9		9,840.60	-		
19	JD	0050				01/03/2016	O/Bal	26,882.08	0.00		Y	26,882.08			
		19	0050	0	Opening Balance			26,882.08	0.00	T9		26,882.08	-		
20	JC	9998				01/03/2016	O/Bal	26,882.08	0.00		Y	26,882.08			
		20	9998	0	Opening Balance			26,882.08	0.00	T9		26,882.08	-		
21	JC	0051				01/03/2016	O/Bal	10,752.83	0.00		Y	10,752.83			
		21	0051	0	Opening Balance			10,752.83	0.00	T9		10,752.83	-		
22	JD	9998				01/03/2016	O/Bal	10,752.83	0.00		Y	10,752.83			
		22	9998	0	Opening Balance			10,752.83	0.00	T9		10,752.83	-		
23	JC	2200				01/03/2016	O/Bal	9,800.00	0.00		Y	9,800.00			
		23	2200	0	Opening Balance			9,800.00	0.00	T9		9,800.00	-		
24	JD	9998				01/03/2016	O/Bal	9,800.00	0.00		Y	9,800.00			
		24	9998	0	Opening Balance			9,800.00	0.00	T9		9,800.00	-		
25	JD	2201				01/03/2016	O/Bal	5,607.00	0.00		Y	5,607.00			
		25	2201	0	Opening Balance			5,607.00	0.00	T9		5,607.00	-		
26	JC	9998				01/03/2016	O/Bal	5,607.00	0.00		Y	5,607.00			
		26	9998	0	Opening Balance			5,607.00	0.00	T9		5,607.00	-		
27	JC	3000				01/03/2016	O/Bal	48,550.70	0.00		Y	48,550.70			
		27	3000	0	Opening Balance			48,550.70	0.00	T9		48,550.70	-		
28	JD	9998				01/03/2016	O/Bal	48,550.70	0.00		Y	48,550.70			
		28	9998	0	Opening Balance			48,550.70	0.00	T9		48,550.70	-		
29	SI	TOW001				03/03/2016	TOW001/I	15,780.00	3,156.00		N	0.00	-		
		29	4000	0	Decorating services			15,780.00	3,156.00	T1		0.00	N		

| Date: | | | | | | | | Dolby Decorating | | | | | | Page: 3 |
| Time: | | | | | | | | Audit Trail (Detailed) | | | | | | |

No	Type	A/C	N/C	Dept	Details	Date	Ref	Net	Tax	T/C	Pd	Paid	V	B	Bank Rec.
30	SI	TOW001				03/03/2016	TOW001/I	2,010.00	402.00		N	0.00	-		
		30	4001	0	Decorating supplies			2,010.00	402.00	T1		0.00	N		
31	SI	LIM001				04/03/2016	LIM001/IN	1,407.00	281.40		Y	1,688.40	-		
		31	4000	0	Decorating services			800.00	160.00	T1		960.00	N		
					97.20 from SC 34	05/03/2016	LIM001/C125					97.20			
					862.80 from SR 49	10/03/2016	BACS					862.80			
		32	4001	0	Decorating supplies			607.00	121.40	T1		728.40	N		
					728.40 from SR 49	10/03/2016	BACS					728.40			
33	SI	BIN001				20/03/2016	BIN001/IN	7,093.10	1,418.62		N	0.00	-		
		33	4000	0	Decorating services			7,093.10	1,418.62	T1		0.00	N		
34	SC	LIM001				05/03/2016	LIM001/C	81.00	16.20		Y	97.20	-		
		34	4001	0	Decorating supplies			81.00	16.20	T1		97.20	N		
					97.20 to SI 31	05/03/2016	LIM001/IN301					97.20			
35	SC	TOW001				23/03/2016	TOW001/	4,000.00	800.00		N	0.00	-		
		35	4001	0	Decorating supplies			4,000.00	800.00	T1		0.00	N		
36	PI	WAL001				02/03/2016	INV2978	1,560.00	312.00		Y	1,872.00	-		
		36	5000	0	Wallpaper			1,250.00	250.00	T1		1,500.00	N		
					24.00 from PC 42	14/03/2016	CN622					24.00			
					110.78 from PC 43	14/03/2016	CN622					110.78			
					1365.22 from PP 53	22/03/2016	BACS					1,365.22			
		37	5001	0	Decorating supplies			310.00	62.00	T1		372.00	N		
					372.00 from PP 53	22/03/2016	BACS					372.00			
38	PI	CAM001				05/03/2016	D03024	3,261.84	652.37		N	0.00	-		
		38	5000	0	Wallpaper			2,620.84	524.17	T1		0.00	N		
		39	5001	0	Decorating supplies			641.00	128.20	T1		0.00	N		
40	PI	ARN001				07/03/2016	PI 419	1,075.80	215.16		N	0.00	-		
		40	5000	0	Wallpaper			1,021.00	204.20	T1		0.00	N		
		41	5001	0	Decorating supplies			54.80	10.96	T1		0.00	N		
42	PC	WAL001				14/03/2016	CN622	112.32	22.46		Y	134.78	-		
		42	5000	0	Wallpaper returned			20.00	4.00	T1		24.00	N		
					24.00 to PI 36	14/03/2016	INV2978					24.00			
		43	5001	0	Decorating supplies			92.32	18.46	T1		110.78	N		
					110.78 to PI 36	14/03/2016	INV2978					110.78			
44	PC	ARN001				18/03/2016	84	31.68	6.34		N	0.00	-		
		44	5000	0	Wallpaper returned			31.68	6.34	T1		0.00	N		
45	BP	1200				21/03/2016	Cash	175.00	0.00		Y	175.00	R		31/03/2016
		45	3050	0	Cash withdrawn for			175.00	0.00	T9		175.00	-		
46	BP	1200				30/03/2016	BACS	4,980.00	0.00		Y	4,980.00	R		31/03/2016
		46	7004	0	Monthly wages			4,980.00	0.00	T9		4,980.00	-		
47	BR	1200				13/03/2016	87	432.50	86.50		Y	519.00	R		31/03/2016
		47	4001	0	Decorating supplies - cash			432.50	86.50	T1		519.00	N		
48	SR	BIN001				02/03/2016	BACS	12,404.40	0.00		Y	12,404.40	R		31/03/2016
		48	1200	0	Sales Receipt			12,404.40	0.00	T9		12,404.40	-		
					12404.40 to SI 1	02/03/2016	O/Bal					12,404.40			
49	SR	LIM001				10/03/2016	BACS	1,591.20	0.00		Y	1,591.20	R		31/03/2016
		49	1200	0	Sales Receipt			1,591.20	0.00	T9		1,591.20	-		
					862.80 to SI 31	10/03/2016	LIM001/IN301					862.80			
					728.40 to SI 32	10/03/2016	LIM001/IN301					728.40			
50	SR	LIM001				24/03/2016	BACS	1,605.95	0.00		Y	1,605.95	R		31/03/2016
		50	1200	0	Sales Receipt			1,605.95	0.00	T9		1,605.95	-		
					1605.95 to SI 2	24/03/2016	O/Bal					1,605.95			
51	SA	TOW001				27/03/2016	Cheque	5,000.00	0.00		N	0.00	N		
		51	1200	0	Payment on Account			5,000.00	0.00	T9		0.00	-		
52	PA	ARN001				20/03/2016	020784	1,500.00	0.00		N	0.00	R		31/03/2016
		52	1200	0	Payment on Account			1,500.00	0.00	T9		0.00	-		
53	PP	WAL001				22/03/2016	BACS	1,737.22	0.00		Y	1,737.22	R		31/03/2016
		53	1200	0	Purchase Payment			1,737.22	0.00	T9		1,737.22	-		
					1365.22 to PI 36	22/03/2016	INV2978					1,365.22			
					372.00 to PI 37	22/03/2016	INV2978					372.00			
54	PP	CAM001				23/03/2016	020785	4,900.50	0.00		Y	4,900.50	R		31/03/2016
		54	1200	0	Purchase Payment			4,900.50	0.00	T9		4,900.50	-		
					4900.50 to PI 5	23/03/2016	O/Bal					4,900.50			
55	BP	1200				18/03/2016	DD	84.00	16.80		Y	100.80	R		31/03/2016
		55	7550	0	TK Telephones			84.00	16.80	T1		100.80	N		
56	BP	1200				20/03/2016	STO	106.00	21.20		Y	127.20	R		31/03/2016
		56	7702	0	Moorhall Rental -			106.00	21.20	T1		127.20	N		
57	JC	1200				01/03/2016	020783	50.00	0.00		Y	50.00	R		31/03/2016
		57	1200	0	Bank Transfer			50.00	0.00	T9		50.00	-		
58	JD	1230				01/03/2016	020783	50.00	0.00		Y	50.00	-		
		58	1230	0	Bank Transfer			50.00	0.00	T9		50.00	-		
59	CP	1230				03/03/2016	184	4.67	0.93		Y	5.60	-		

No	Type	A/C	N/C	Dept	Details	Date	Ref	Net	Tax	T/C	Pd	Paid	V	B	Bank Rec.

Date:
Time:

Dolby Decorating
Audit Trail (Detailed)

Page: 5

No	Type	A/C	N/C	Dept	Details	Date	Ref	Net	Tax	T/C	Pd	Paid	V	B	Bank Rec.
		59	7502	0	x4 boxes of pens			4.67	0.93	T1		5.60	N		
60	CP	1230				09/03/2016	185	6.20	1.24		Y	7.44			
		60	7801	0	Cleaning materials			6.20	1.24	T1		7.44	N		
61	CP	1230				15/03/2016	186	7.50	0.00		Y	7.50			
		61	7501	0	Parcel			7.50	0.00	T2		7.50	N		
62	CP	1230				23/03/2016	187	21.00	0.00		Y	21.00			
		62	7501	0	Postage stamps			21.00	0.00	T2		21.00	N		
63	JD	4001				30/03/2016	006	46.00	0.00		Y	46.00			
		63	4001	0	Correction of error			46.00	0.00	T9		46.00	-		
64	JC	4000				30/03/2016	006	46.00	0.00		Y	46.00			
		64	4000	0	Correction of error			46.00	0.00	T9		46.00	-		
65	BP	1200				31/03/2016	DD	18.00	0.00		Y	18.00		R	31/03/2016
		65	7901	0	Bank charges			18.00	0.00	T2		18.00	N		
66	BP	1200				26/03/2016	DD	130.00	0.00		Y	130.00		R	31/03/2016
		66	7103	0	Arnold City Council			130.00	0.00	T2		130.00	N		

Evidence 3b – Petty cash account within the nominal ledger, showing all transactions within the account

Date:
Time:

Dolby Decorating
Nominal Activity

Page: 1

Date From:	01/01/1980	**N/C From:**	1230
Date To:	31/03/2016	**N/C To:**	1230
Transaction From:	1		
Transaction To:	99,999,999		

N/C: 1230 **Name:** Petty Cash **Account Balance:** 208.46 DR

No	Type	Date	Account	Ref	Details	Dept	T/C	Value	Debit	Credit	V	B
9	JD	01/03/2016	1230	O/Bal	Opening Balance	0	T9	200.00	200.00		-	-
58	JD	01/03/2016	1230	020783	Bank Transfer	0	T9	50.00	50.00		-	-
59	CP	03/03/2016	1230	184	x4 boxes of pens	0	T1	5.60		5.60	N	-
60	CP	09/03/2016	1230	185	Cleaning materials	0	T1	7.44		7.44	N	-
61	CP	15/03/2016	1230	186	Parcel	0	T2	7.50		7.50	N	-
62	CP	23/03/2016	1230	187	Postage stamps	0	T2	21.00		21.00	N	-
					Totals:				250.00	41.54		
					History Balance:				208.46			

Evidence 4 – Trial balance as at 31 March 20-X

Date:			Page: 1
Time:	**Dolby Decorating**		
	Period Trial Balance		

To Period: Month 1, March 2016

N/C	Name	Debit	Credit
0020	Plant and Machinery	25,600.00	
0021	Plant/Machinery Depreciation		12,800.00
0040	Furniture and Fixtures	32,802.00	
0041	Furniture/Fixture Depreciation		9,840.60
0050	Motor Vehicles	26,882.08	
0051	Motor Vehicles Depreciation		10,752.83
1100	Debtors Control Account	23,539.72	
1200	Bank Current Account	3,941.83	
1230	Petty Cash	208.46	
2100	Creditors Control Account		12,143.95
2200	Sales Tax Control Account		14,328.32
2201	Purchase Tax Control Account	6,797.90	
3000	Capital		48,550.70
3050	Drawings	175.00	
4000	Sales - Decorating services		23,719.10
4001	Sales - Decorating supplies	1,077.50	
5000	Materials Purchased (Wallpaper)	4,840.16	
5001	Materials Purchased (Decorating Supplies)	913.48	
7004	Wages - Regular	4,980.00	
7103	General Rates	130.00	
7501	Postage and Carriage	28.50	
7502	Office Stationery	4.67	
7550	Telephone and Fax	84.00	
7702	Equipment Leasing	106.00	
7801	Cleaning	6.20	
7901	Bank Charges	18.00	
	Totals:	132,135.50	132,135.50

Evidence 5a – Screenshot of the recurring entry set up screen, including all relevant input detail

Evidence 5b – Screenshot of the recurring entry set up screen, including all relevant input detail

Task 13 – Evidence 6 – Screenshot of the bank reconciliation screen showing reconciled items

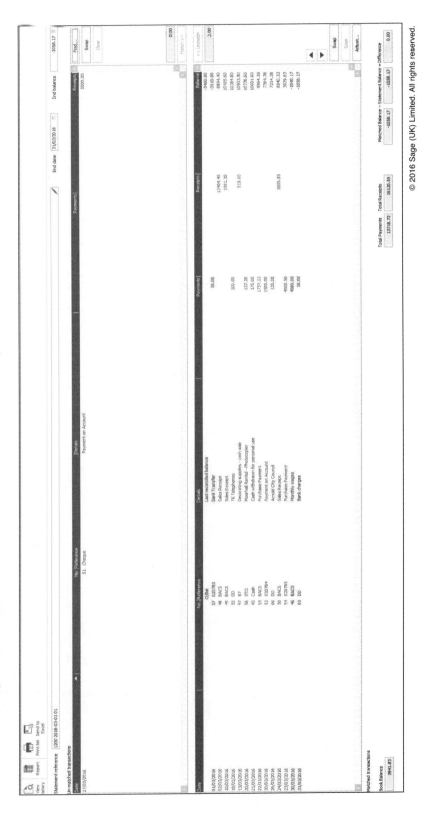

or

No	Type	Date	A/C	N/C	Dept	Ref	Details	Net	Tax	T/C

Date: **Dolby Decorating**   **Page:** 1
Time: **Bank Reconciled Transactions**

Bank Reconciled On: 01/03/2016

No	Type	Date	A/C	N/C	Dept	Ref	Details	Net	Tax	T/C
7	JC	01/03/2016	1200	1200	0	O/Bal	Opening Balance	3,460.00	0.00	T9

Bank Reconciled On: 31/03/2016

No	Type	Date	A/C	N/C	Dept	Ref	Details	Net	Tax	T/C
45	BP	21/03/2016	1200	3050	0	Cash	Cash withdrawn for	175.00	0.00	T9
46	BP	30/03/2016	1200	7004	0	BACS	Monthly wages	4,980.00	0.00	T9
47	BR	13/03/2016	1200	4001	0	87	Decorating supplies - cash	432.50	86.50	T1
48	SR	02/03/2016	BIN001	1200	0	BACS	Sales Receipt	12,404.40	0.00	T9
49	SR	10/03/2016	LIM001	1200	0	BACS	Sales Receipt	1,591.20	0.00	T9
50	SR	24/03/2016	LIM001	1200	0	BACS	Sales Receipt	1,605.95	0.00	T9
52	PA	20/03/2016	ARN001	1200	0	020784	Payment on Account	1,500.00	0.00	T9
53	PP	22/03/2016	WAL001	1200	0	BACS	Purchase Payment	1,737.22	0.00	T9
54	PP	23/03/2016	CAM001	1200	0	020785	Purchase Payment	4,900.50	0.00	T9
55	BP	18/03/2016	1200	7550	0	DD	TK Telephones	84.00	16.80	T1
56	BP	20/03/2016	1200	7702	0	STO	Moorhall Rental -	106.00	21.20	T1
57	JC	01/03/2016	1200	1200	0	020783	Bank Transfer	50.00	0.00	T9
65	BP	31/03/2016	1200	7901	0	DD	Bank charges	18.00	0.00	T2
66	BP	26/03/2016	1200	7103	0	DD	Arnold City Council	130.00	0.00	T2

Answers to practice assessment 3

Task	Transaction Type	Account(s)		Date 20-X	Net Amount £	VAT £	Allocated against receipt/ Payment ✓	Reconciled with bank statement ✓
1	Customer O/bal	AGC01		1 July	4,210.32		✓	
	Customer O/bal	BGC01		1 July	262.50			
	Customer O/bal	CC01		1 July	1,798.75		✓	
	Customer O/bal	MP01		1 July	3,475.20		✓	
2	Supplier O/bal	BW01		1 July	6,203.00		✓	
	Supplier O/bal	JFCS01		1 July	2,004.24			
	Supplier O/bal	SCS01		1 July	741.00		✓	
	Supplier O/bal	WW01		1 July	6,410.00		✓	
3	Dr	Bank current account		1 July	4,840.20			✓
	Dr	Bank deposit account		1 July	6,000.00			
	Dr	Petty cash		1 July	50.00			
	Dr	Furniture – cost		1 July	34,650.00			
	Cr	Furniture – accumulated depreciation		1 July	5,197.50			
	Dr	Sales ledger control *		1 July	9,746.77			
	Cr	Purchase ledger control *		1 July	15,358.24			
	Cr	VAT on sales		1 July	8,780.00			
	Dr	VAT on purchases		1 July	1,640.00			
	Cr	Capital		1 July	27,591.23			
		*If appropriate						
4	Sales inv	AGC01	Sales:	2 July				
			Gift wrap		64.00	12.80	✓	
			Decorations		50.00	10.00	✓	
			Decoration		600.00	120.00	✓	
	Sales inv	MP01	Sales:	6 July				
			Greetings cards		3,100.00	620.00		
			Decorations		60.00	12.00		
	Sales inv	BGC01	Sales:	6 July				
			Decorations		123.00	24.60	✓	
			Decorations		275.00	55.00	✓	
			Greetings cards		660.00	132.00	✓	
	Sales CN	CC01	Sales:	8 July	22.00	4.40	✓	
			Greetings cards					
5	Purchase inv	JFCS01	Purchases	3 July				
			Gift cards		427.29	85.46		
			Decorations		3,844.00	768.80		
	Purchase inv	WW01	Purchases	10 July				
			Gift cards		2,970.05	594.01		
	Purchase inv	SCS01	Purchases	12 July				
			Decorations		1,333.40	266.68	✓	
	Purchase inv	WW01	Purchases	13 July				
			Gift cards		200.00	40.00		
			Decorations		341.30	68.26		
	Purchase CN	SCS01	Purchase returns	14 July				
			Gift cards		74.22	14.84	✓	
			Decorations		100.00	20.00	✓	
	Purchase CN	BW01	Purchase returns	16 July				
			Decorations		57.80	11.56		

6	Bank receipt	Bank	Online sales	8 July	3,002.25	600.45			✓
	Bank receipt	Bank	Online sales	15 July	2,748.00	549.60			✓
	Bank receipt	Bank	Online sales	22 July	1,580.00	316.00			✓
	Bank receipt	Bank	Online sales	29 July	2,451.00	490.20			✓
	Bank payment	Bank	Furniture	10 July	1,116.67	223.33			✓
	Bank payment	Bank	Purchases	14 July	249.17	49.83			✓
	Bank payment	Bank	Advertising	16 July	642.00	128.40			✓
7	Customer receipt	MP01	Bank	10 July	3,475.20			✓	✓
	Customer receipt	CC01	Bank	13 July	1,772.35			✓	✓
	Customer receipt	AGC01	Bank	14 July	4,210.32			✓	✓
	Customer receipt	AGC01	Bank	30 July	1,200.00				✓
	Customer receipt	BGC01	Bank	24 July	1,269.60			✓	✓
8	Supplier payment	SCS01	Bank	22 July	2,132.02			✓	✓
	Supplier payment	BW01	Bank	23 July	6,203.00			✓	✓
	Supplier payment	WW01	Bank	23 July	6,410.00			✓	
9	Bank payment	Bank	General rates – DD	15 July	132.40				✓
10	Cash payment	Petty cash	Cleaning	5 July	10.17	2.03			
	Cash payment	Petty cash	Donation	6 July	15.00				
	Cash payment	Petty cash	Travel	10 July	14.80				
	Cash payment	Petty cash	Office stationery	10 July	5.20	1.04			
	Cr	Bank		11 July	48.24				✓
	Dr	Petty cash		11 July	48.24				
11	Journal debit	Office equipment		30 July	3,748.00				
	Journal credit	Furniture		30 July	3,478.00				
12	Supplier payment	AGC01	Bank	5 July	856.80			✓	✓
	Bank payment	Bank	Bank charges	30 July	22.00				✓

Evidence 1a – All customer transactions

Date:						**Clifton Card Warehouse**					**Page:**	1
Time:						**Customer Activity (Detailed)**						

Date From:	01/01/1980					**Customer From:**	
Date To:	31/07/2016					**Customer To:**	ZZZZZZZZ
Transaction From:	1					**N/C From:**	
Transaction To:	99,999,999					**N/C To:**	99999999
Inc b/fwd transaction:	No					**Dept From:**	0
Exc later payment:	No					**Dept To:**	999

** **NOTE: All report values are shown in Base Currency, unless otherwise indicated** **

A/C: AGC01 **Name:** Ashford Gift Centre   **Contact:** Phoebe May   **Tel:** 0145 652798

No	Type	Date	Ref	N/C	Details	Dept	T/C	Value	O/S	Debit	Credit	V	B
1	SI	01/07/2016	O/Bal	9998	Opening Balance	0	T9	4,210.32		4,210.32		-	-
25	SI	02/07/2016	00895	4001	Wrapping paper	0	T1	76.80		76.80		N	-
26	SI	02/07/2016	00895	4002	Blue balloons	0	T1	60.00		60.00		N	-
27	SI	02/07/2016	00895	4002	Helium balloons	0	T1	720.00		720.00		N	-
52	SR	14/07/2016	BACS	1200	Sales Receipt	0	T9	4,210.32			4,210.32	-	R
53	SA	30/07/2016	BACS	1200	Payment on Account	0	T9	1,200.00 *	-1,200.00		1,200.00	-	R
68	SR	05/07/2016	BACS	1200	Sales Receipt	0	T9	856.80			856.80	-	R
							Totals:	-1,200.00	-1,200.00	5,067.12	6,267.12		

Amount Outstanding	-1,200.00
Amount Paid this period	6,267.12
Credit Limit £	5,200.00
Turnover YTD	4,924.32

A/C: BGC01 **Name:** Brooklane Garden Centre   **Contact:** Sarah Miller   **Tel:** 0145 758201

No	Type	Date	Ref	N/C	Details	Dept	T/C	Value	O/S	Debit	Credit	V	B
2	SI	01/07/2016	O/Bal	9998	Opening Balance	0	T9	262.50 *	262.50	262.50		-	-
30	SI	06/07/2016	00897	4002	Candles	0	T1	147.60		147.60		N	-
31	SI	06/07/2016	00897	4002	Table decorations	0	T1	330.00		330.00		N	-
32	SI	06/07/2016	00897	4000	Greetings cards	0	T1	792.00		792.00		N	-
54	SR	24/07/2016	Cheque	1200	Sales Receipt	0	T9	1,269.60			1,269.60	-	R
							Totals:	262.50	262.50	1,532.10	1,269.60		

Amount Outstanding	262.50
Amount Paid this period	1,269.60
Credit Limit £	7,500.00
Turnover YTD	1,320.50

A/C: CC01 **Name:** Cossall Cards   **Contact:** Agnes Nowak   **Tel:** 0152 415234

No	Type	Date	Ref	N/C	Details	Dept	T/C	Value	O/S	Debit	Credit	V	B
3	SI	01/07/2016	O/Bal	9998	Opening Balance	0	T9	1,798.75		1,798.75		-	-
33	SC	08/07/2016	0074	4000	Damaged cards returned	0	T1	26.40			26.40	N	-
51	SR	13/07/2016	BACS	1200	Sales Receipt	0	T9	1,772.35			1,772.35	-	R
							Totals:	0.00	0.00	1,798.75	1,798.75		

Amount Outstanding	0.00
Amount Paid this period	1,772.35
Credit Limit £	3,000.00
Turnover YTD	1,776.75

A/C: MP01 **Name:** Michelle Proctor Ltd   **Contact:** Raj Singh   **Tel:** 0152 778995

No	Type	Date	Ref	N/C	Details	Dept	T/C	Value	O/S	Debit	Credit	V	B
4	SI	01/07/2016	O/Bal	9998	Opening Balance	0	T9	3,475.20		3,475.20		-	-
28	SI	06/07/2016	00896	4000	Greetings cards	0	T1	3,720.00 *	3,720.00	3,720.00		N	-
29	SI	06/07/2016	00896	4002	Banners	0	T1	72.00 *	72.00	72.00		N	-
50	SR	10/07/2016	BACS	1200	Sales Receipt	0	T9	3,475.20			3,475.20	-	R
							Totals:	3,792.00	3,792.00	7,267.20	3,475.20		

Amount Outstanding	3,792.00
Amount Paid this period	3,475.20
Credit Limit £	9,700.00
Turnover YTD	6,635.20

Evidence 1b – Balance owed by each customer

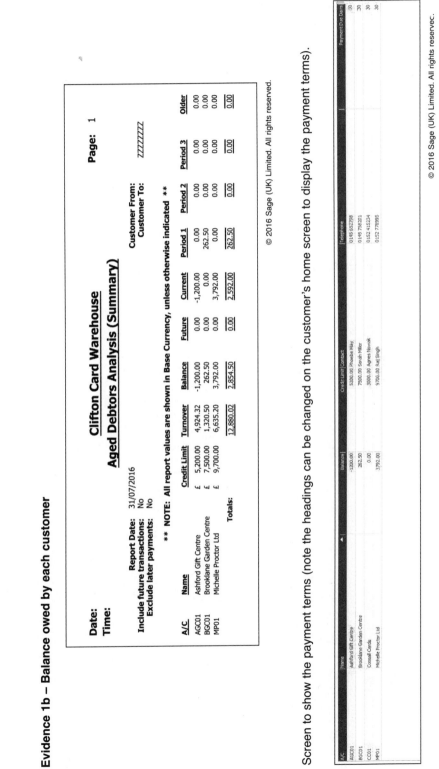

Clifton Card Warehouse

Aged Debtors Analysis (Summary)

Page: 1

| Date: | | | | | | Customer From: | | | |
| Time: | | | | | | Customer To: | | | ZZZZZZZ |

Report Date: 31/07/2016
Include future transactions: No
Exclude later payments: No

** NOTE: All report values are shown in Base Currency, unless otherwise indicated **

A/C	Name		Credit Limit	Turnover	Balance	Future	Current	Period 1	Period 2	Period 3	Older
AGC01	Ashford Gift Centre	£	5,200.00	4,924.32	-1,200.00	0.00	-1,200.00	0.00	0.00	0.00	0.00
BGC01	Brooklane Garden Centre	£	7,500.00	1,320.50	262.50	0.00	0.00	262.50	0.00	0.00	0.00
MP01	Michelle Proctor Ltd	£	9,700.00	6,635.20	3,792.00	0.00	3,792.00	0.00	0.00	0.00	0.00
	Totals:			12,880.02	2,854.50	0.00	2,592.00	262.50	0.00	0.00	0.00

Screen to show the payment terms (note the headings can be changed on the customer's home screen to display the payment terms).

A/C	Name	Balance	Credit Limit	Contact	Telephone	Payment Due Days
AGC01	Ashford Gift Centre	-1200.00	5200.00	Phoebe May	0145 652298	30
BGC01	Brooklane Garden Centre	262.50	7500.00	Sarah Miller	0145 758201	30
CC01	Consall Cards	0.00	3000.00	Agnes Nowak	0152 415224	30
MP01	Michelle Proctor Ltd	3792.00	9700.00	Raj Singh	0152 778995	30

Evidence 1c – Statement of account for Michelle Proctor Ltd

Clifton Card Warehouse
340 Briarwood Road
Granby
GD7 6CA

MP01

Michelle Proctor Ltd   31/07/2016
414 Cardale Road

Granby

GB7 5RD

All values are shown in Pound Sterling

01/07/2016	O/Bal	Goods/Services	£	3,475.20			£	3,475.20
06/07/2016	00896	Goods/Services	£	3,792.00			£	7,267.20
10/07/2016	BACS	Payment			£	3,475.20	£	3,792.00

£	3,792.00	£	0.00	£	0.00	£	0.00	£	0.00	**£**	**3,792.00**

Evidence 2a – All supplier transactions

Date:	**Clifton Card Warehouse**
Time:	**Supplier Activity (Detailed)**

Date From:	01/01/1980	**Supplier From:**	
Date To:	31/07/2016	**Supplier To:**	ZZZZZZZZ
Transaction From:	1	**N/C From:**	
Transaction To:	99,999,999	**N/C To:**	99999999
Inc b/fwd transaction:	No	**Dept From:**	0
Exc later payment:	No	**Dept To:**	999

Page: 1

** NOTE: All report values are shown in Base Currency, unless otherwise indicated **

A/C: BW01   **Name:** Burton Wholesale   **Contact:** Priya Malik   **Tel:** 0123 142124

No	Type	Date	Ref	N/C	Details	Dept	T/C	Value	O/S	Debit	Credit	V	B
5	PI	01/07/2016	O/Bal	9998	Opening Balance	0	T9	6,203.00	0.00		6,203.00	-	-
42	PC	16/07/2016	36	5001	Decorations/Gift wrap	0	T1	69.36 *	-69.36	69.36		N	-
56	PP	23/07/2016	024230	1200	Purchase Payment	0	T9	6,203.00	0.00	6,203.00		-	R
					Totals:			-69.36	-69.36	6,272.36	6,203.00		

Amount Outstanding	-69.36
Amount paid this period	6,203.00
Credit Limit £	12,300.00
Turnover YTD	6,145.20

A/C: JFCS01   **Name:** JF Card Supplies   **Contact:** Jasmin Fisher   **Tel:** 0123 872365

No	Type	Date	Ref	N/C	Details	Dept	T/C	Value	O/S	Debit	Credit	V	B
6	PI	01/07/2016	O/Bal	9998	Opening Balance	0	T9	2,004.24 *	2,004.24		2,004.24	-	-
34	PI	03/07/2016	INV3079	5000	Gift cards	0	T1	512.75 *	512.75		512.75	N	-
35	PI	03/07/2016	INV3079	5001	Decorations/Gift wrap	0	T1	4,612.80 *	4,612.80		4,612.80	N	-
					Totals:			7,129.79	7,129.79	0.00	7,129.79		

Amount Outstanding	7,129.79
Amount paid this period	0.00
Credit Limit £	7,500.00
Turnover YTD	6,275.53

A/C: SCS01   **Name:** Stonebridge Card Supplies   **Contact:** Samia Masood   **Tel:** 0123 874215

No	Type	Date	Ref	N/C	Details	Dept	T/C	Value	O/S	Debit	Credit	V	B
7	PI	01/07/2016	O/Bal	9998	Opening Balance	0	T9	741.00	0.00		741.00	-	-
37	PI	12/07/2016	1784	5001	Decorations/Gift wrap	0	T1	1,600.08	0.00		1,600.08	N	-
40	PC	14/07/2016	CN41	5000	Gift cards returned	0	T1	89.06	0.00	89.06		N	-
41	PC	14/07/2016	CN41	5001	Decorations/Gift wrap	0	T1	120.00	0.00	120.00		N	-
55	PP	22/07/2016	024229	1200	Purchase Payment	0	T9	2,132.02	0.00	2,132.02		-	R
					Totals:			0.00	0.00	2,341.08	2,341.08		

Amount Outstanding	0.00
Amount paid this period	2,132.02
Credit Limit £	3,000.00
Turnover YTD	1,900.18

A/C: WW01   **Name:** Woolerton Warehouse   **Contact:** Emilie Durand   **Tel:** 0152 748214

No	Type	Date	Ref	N/C	Details	Dept	T/C	Value	O/S	Debit	Credit	V	B
8	PI	01/07/2016	O/Bal	9998	Opening Balance	0	T9	6,410.00	0.00		6,410.00	-	-
36	PI	10/07/2016	WW417	5000	Gift cards	0	T1	3,564.06 *	3,564.06		3,564.06	N	-
38	PI	13/07/2016	32546	5000	Gift cards	0	T1	240.00 *	240.00		240.00	N	-
39	PI	13/07/2016	32546	5001	Decorations/Gift wrap	0	T1	409.56 *	409.56		409.56	N	-
57	PP	23/07/2016	024231	1200	Purchase Payment	0	T9	6,410.00	0.00	6,410.00		-	N
					Totals:			4,213.62	4,213.62	6,410.00	10,623.62		

Amount Outstanding	4,213.62
Amount paid this period	6,410.00
Credit Limit £	11,000.00
Turnover YTD	9,921.35

Evidence 2b – Balance owed by suppliers

Clifton Card Warehouse
Aged Creditors Analysis (Summary)

Page: 1

Date:
Time:

Report Date: 31/07/2016
Include future transactions: No
Exclude Later Payments: No

Supplier From:
Supplier To: ZZZZZZZZ

** NOTE: All report values are shown in Base Currency, unless otherwise indicated **

A/C	Name	Credit Limit	Turnover	Balance	Future	Current	Period 1	Period 2	Period 3	Older
BW01	Burton Wholesale	£ 12,300.00	6,145.20	-69.36	0.00	-69.36	0.00	0.00	0.00	0.00
JFCS01	JF Card Supplies	£ 7,500.00	6,275.53	7,129.79	0.00	5,125.55	2,004.24	0.00	0.00	0.00
WW01	Woolerton Warehouse	£ 11,000.00	9,921.35	4,213.62	0.00	4,213.62	0.00	0.00	0.00	0.00
	Totals:		22,342.08	11,274.05	0.00	9,269.81	2,004.24	0.00	0.00	0.00

Screen to show the payment terms (note the headings can be changed on the supplier's home screen to display the payment terms).

A/C	Name	Balance	Credit Limit	Contact	Telephone	Payment Due
BW01	Burton Wholesale	-69.36	12300.00	Priya Malik	0123 342124	30
JFCS01	JF Card Supplies	7129.79	7500.00	Jasmin Fisher	0123 872365	30
SCS01	Stonebridge Card Supplies	0.00	3000.00	Samia Masood	0123 874215	30
WW01	Woolerton Warehouse	4213.62	11000.00	Emilie Durand	0152 748214	30

Evidence 3 – An audit trail, showing full details of all transactions, including details of receipts/payments allocated to items in customer/supplier accounts and details of items in the bank account that have been reconciled.

Date: Time:						**Clifton Card Warehouse** **Audit Trail (Detailed)**							Page: 1	
Date From: 01/01/1980											**Customer From:**			
Date To: 31/12/2019											**Customer To:** ZZZZZZZZ			
Transaction From: 1											**Supplier From:**			
Transaction To: 99,999,999											**Supplier To:** ZZZZZZZZ			
Exclude Deleted Tran: No														

No	Type	A/C	N/C	Dept	Details	Date	Ref	Net	Tax	T/C	Pd	Paid	V	B	Bank Rec.
1	SI	AGC01				01/07/2016	O/Bal	4,210.32	0.00		Y	4,210.32	-		
		1	9998	0	Opening Balance			4,210.32	0.00	T9		4,210.32	-		
					4210.32 from SR 52	14/07/2016	BACS					4,210.32			
2	SI	BGC01				01/07/2016	O/Bal	262.50	0.00		N	0.00			
		2	9998	0	Opening Balance			262.50	0.00	T9		0.00	-		
3	SI	CC01				01/07/2016	O/Bal	1,798.75	0.00		Y	1,798.75	-		
		3	9998	0	Opening Balance			1,798.75	0.00	T9		1,798.75	-		
					26.40 from SC 33	08/07/2016	0074					26.40			
					1772.35 from SR 51	13/07/2016	BACS					1,772.35			
4	SI	MP01				01/07/2016	O/Bal	3,475.20	0.00		Y	3,475.20	-		
		4	9998	0	Opening Balance			3,475.20	0.00	T9		3,475.20	-		
					3475.20 from SR 50	10/07/2016	BACS					3,475.20			
5	PI	BW01				01/07/2016	O/Bal	6,203.00	0.00		Y	6,203.00	-		
		5	9998	0	Opening Balance			6,203.00	0.00	T9		6,203.00	-		
					6203.00 from PP 56	23/07/2016	024230					6,203.00			
6	PI	JFCS01				01/07/2016	O/Bal	2,004.24	0.00		N	0.00			
		6	9998	0	Opening Balance			2,004.24	0.00	T9		0.00	-		
7	PI	SCS01				01/07/2016	O/Bal	741.00	0.00		Y	741.00	-		
		7	9998	0	Opening Balance			741.00	0.00	T9		741.00	-		
					89.06 from PC 40	14/07/2016	CN41					89.06			
					120.00 from PC 41	14/07/2016	CN41					120.00			
					531.94 from PP 55	22/07/2016	024229					531.94			
8	PI	WW01				01/07/2016	O/Bal	6,410.00	0.00		Y	6,410.00	-		
		8	9998	0	Opening Balance			6,410.00	0.00	T9		6,410.00	-		
					6410.00 from PP 57	23/07/2016	024231					6,410.00			
9	JD	1200				01/07/2016	O/Bal	4,840.20	0.00		Y	4,840.20	-		01/07/2016
		9	1200	0	Opening Balance			4,840.20	0.00	T9		4,840.20	-		
10	JC	9998				01/07/2016	O/Bal	4,840.20	0.00		Y	4,840.20	-		
		10	9998	0	Opening Balance			4,840.20	0.00	T9		4,840.20	-		

Date: Time:						Clifton Card Warehouse Audit Trail (Detailed)									Page: 2
No	**Type**	**A/C**	**N/C**	**Dept**	**Details**	**Date**	**Ref**	**Net**	**Tax**	**T/C**	**Pd**	**Paid**	**V**	**B**	**Bank Rec.**
11	JD	1210				01/07/2016	O/Bal	6,000.00	0.00		Y	6,000.00		-	01/07/2016
		11	1210	0	Opening Balance			6,000.00	0.00	T9		6,000.00	-		
12	JC	9998				01/07/2016	O/Bal	6,000.00	0.00		Y	6,000.00		-	
		12	9998	0	Opening Balance			6,000.00	0.00	T9		6,000.00	-		
13	JD	1230				01/07/2016	O/Bal	50.00	0.00		Y	50.00		-	01/07/2016
		13	1230	0	Opening Balance			50.00	0.00	T9		50.00	-		
14	JC	9998				01/07/2016	O/Bal	50.00	0.00		Y	50.00		-	
		14	9998	0	Opening Balance			50.00	0.00	T9		50.00	-		
15	JD	0040				01/07/2016	O/Bal	34,650.00	0.00		Y	34,650.00		-	
		15	0040	0	Opening Balance			34,650.00	0.00	T9		34,650.00	-		
16	JC	9998				01/07/2016	O/Bal	34,650.00	0.00		Y	34,650.00		-	
		16	9998	0	Opening Balance			34,650.00	0.00	T9		34,650.00	-		
17	JC	0041				01/07/2016	O/Bal	5,197.50	0.00		Y	5,197.50		-	
		17	0041	0	Opening Balance			5,197.50	0.00	T9		5,197.50	-		
18	JD	9998				01/07/2016	O/Bal	5,197.50	0.00		Y	5,197.50		-	
		18	9998	0	Opening Balance			5,197.50	0.00	T9		5,197.50	-		
19	JC	2200				01/07/2016	O/Bal	8,780.00	0.00		Y	8,780.00		-	
		19	2200	0	Opening Balance			8,780.00	0.00	T9		8,780.00	-		
20	JD	9998				01/07/2016	O/Bal	8,780.00	0.00		Y	8,780.00		-	
		20	9998	0	Opening Balance			8,780.00	0.00	T9		8,780.00	-		
21	JD	2201				01/07/2016	O/Bal	1,640.00	0.00		Y	1,640.00		-	
		21	2201	0	Opening Balance			1,640.00	0.00	T9		1,640.00	-		
22	JC	9998				01/07/2016	O/Bal	1,640.00	0.00		Y	1,640.00		-	
		22	9998	0	Opening Balance			1,640.00	0.00	T9		1,640.00	-		
23	JC	3000				01/07/2016	O/Bal	27,591.23	0.00		Y	27,591.23		-	
		23	3000	0	Opening Balance			27,591.23	0.00	T9		27,591.23	-		
24	JD	9998				01/07/2016	O/Bal	27,591.23	0.00		Y	27,591.23		-	
		24	9998	0	Opening Balance			27,591.23	0.00	T9		27,591.23	-		
25	SI	AGC01				02/07/2016	00895	714.00	142.80		Y	856.80		-	
		25	4001	0	Wrapping paper			64.00	12.80	T1		76.80	N		
					76.80 from SR 68	05/07/2016	BACS					76.80			
		26	4002	0	Blue balloons			50.00	10.00	T1		60.00	N		
					60.00 from SR 68	05/07/2016	BACS					60.00			
		27	4002	0	Helium balloons			600.00	120.00	T1		720.00	N		
					720.00 from SR 68	05/07/2016	BACS					720.00			
28	SI	MP01				06/07/2016	00896	3,160.00	632.00		N	0.00		-	
		28	4000	0	Greetings cards			3,100.00	620.00	T1		0.00	N		
		29	4002	0	Banners			60.00	12.00	T1		0.00	N		
30	SI	BGC01				06/07/2016	00897	1,058.00	211.60		Y	1,269.60		-	
		30	4002	0	Candles			123.00	24.60	T1		147.60	N		
					147.60 from SR 54	24/07/2016	Cheque					147.60			
		31	4002	0	Table decorations			275.00	55.00	T1		330.00	N		
					330.00 from SR 54	24/07/2016	Cheque					330.00			
		32	4000	0	Greetings cards			660.00	132.00	T1		792.00	N		
					792.00 from SR 54	24/07/2016	Cheque					792.00			
33	SC	CC01				08/07/2016	0074	22.00	4.40		Y	26.40		-	
		33	4000	0	Damaged cards returned			22.00	4.40	T1		26.40	N		
					26.40 to SI 3	08/07/2016	O/Bal					26.40			
34	PI	JFCS01				03/07/2016	INV3079	4,271.29	854.26		N	0.00		-	
		34	5000	0	Gift cards			427.29	85.46	T1		0.00	N		
		35	5001	0	Decorations/Gift wrap			3,844.00	768.80	T1		0.00	N		
36	PI	WW01				10/07/2016	WW417	2,970.05	594.01		N	0.00		-	
		36	5000	0	Gift cards			2,970.05	594.01	T1		0.00	N		
37	PI	SCS01				12/07/2016	1784	1,333.40	266.68		Y	1,600.08		-	
		37	5001	0	Decorations/Gift wrap			1,333.40	266.68	T1		1,600.08	N		
					1600.08 from PP 55	22/07/2016	024229					1,600.08			
38	PI	WW01				13/07/2016	32546	541.30	108.26		N	0.00		-	
		38	5000	0	Gift cards			200.00	40.00	T1		0.00	N		
		39	5001	0	Decorations/Gift wrap			341.30	68.26	T1		0.00	N		
40	PC	SCS01				14/07/2016	CN41	174.22	34.84		Y	209.06		-	
		40	5000	0	Gift cards returned			74.22	14.84	T1		89.06	N		
					89.06 to PI 7	14/07/2016	O/Bal					89.06			
		41	5001	0	Decorations/Gift wrap			100.00	20.00	T1		120.00	N		
					120.00 to PI 7	14/07/2016	O/Bal					120.00			
42	PC	BW01				16/07/2016	36	57.80	11.56		N	0.00		-	
		42	5001	0	Decorations/Gift wrap			57.80	11.56	T1		0.00	N		
43	BR	1200				08/07/2016		3,002.25	600.45		Y	3,602.70		R	31/07/2016
		43	4003	0	Online cash sales			3,002.25	600.45	T1		3,602.70	N		
44	BR	1200				15/07/2016		2,748.00	549.60		Y	3,297.60		R	31/07/2016
		44	4003	0	Online cash sales			2,748.00	549.60	T1		3,297.60	N		

| Date: | | | | Clifton Card Warehouse | | | | | | | | Page: 4 | | | |
| Time: | | | | Audit Trail (Detailed) | | | | | | | | | | | |

No	Type	A/C	N/C	Dept	Details	Date	Ref	Net	Tax	T/C	Pd	Paid	V	B	Bank Rec.
45	BR	1200				22/07/2016		1,580.00	316.00		Y	1,896.00		R	31/07/2016
		45	4003	0	Online cash sales			1,580.00	316.00	T1		1,896.00	N		
46	BR	1200				29/07/2016		2,451.00	490.20		Y	2,941.20		R	31/07/2016
		46	4003	0	Online cash sales			2,451.00	490.20	T1		2,941.20	N		
47	BP	1200				10/07/2016	024226	1,116.67	223.33		Y	1,340.00		R	31/07/2016
		47	0040	0	Table and shelving			1,116.67	223.33	T1		1,340.00	N		
48	BP	1200				14/07/2016	024227	249.17	49.83		Y	299.00		R	31/07/2016
		48	5000	0	Greetings cards Cromford			249.17	49.83	T1		299.00	N		
49	BP	1200				16/07/2016	024228	642.00	128.40		Y	770.40		R	31/07/2016
		49	6201	0	Granby news article			642.00	128.40	T1		770.40	N		
50	SR	MP01				10/07/2016	BACS	3,475.20	0.00		Y	3,475.20		R	31/07/2016
		50	1200	0	Sales Receipt			3,475.20	0.00	T9		3,475.20	-		
					3475.20 to SI 4	10/07/2016	O/Bal					3,475.20			
51	SR	CC01				13/07/2016	BACS	1,772.35	0.00		Y	1,772.35		R	31/07/2016
		51	1200	0	Sales Receipt			1,772.35	0.00	T9		1,772.35	-		
					1772.35 to SI 3	13/07/2016	O/Bal					1,772.35			
52	SR	AGC01				14/07/2016	BACS	4,210.32	0.00		Y	4,210.32		R	31/07/2016
		52	1200	0	Sales Receipt			4,210.32	0.00	T9		4,210.32	-		
					4210.32 to SI 1	14/07/2016	O/Bal					4,210.32			
53	SA	AGC01				30/07/2016	BACS	1,200.00	0.00		N	0.00		R	31/07/2016
		53	1200	0	Payment on Account			1,200.00	0.00	T9		0.00	-		
54	SR	BGC01				24/07/2016	Cheque	1,269.60	0.00		Y	1,269.60		R	31/07/2016
		54	1200	0	Sales Receipt			1,269.60	0.00	T9		1,269.60	-		
					147.60 to SI 30	24/07/2016	00897					147.60			
					330.00 to SI 31	24/07/2016	00897					330.00			
					792.00 to SI 32	24/07/2016	00897					792.00			
55	PP	SCS01				22/07/2016	024229	2,132.02	0.00		Y	2,132.02		R	31/07/2016
		55	1200	0	Purchase Payment			2,132.02	0.00	T9		2,132.02	-		
					531.94 to PI 7	22/07/2016	O/Bal					531.94			
					1600.08 to PI 37	22/07/2016	1784					1,600.08			
56	PP	BW01				23/07/2016	024230	6,203.00	0.00		Y	6,203.00		R	31/07/2016
		56	1200	0	Purchase Payment			6,203.00	0.00	T9		6,203.00	-		
					6203.00 to PI 5	23/07/2016	O/Bal					6,203.00			
57	PP	WW01				23/07/2016	024231	6,410.00	0.00		Y	6,410.00		N	
		57	1200	0	Purchase Payment			6,410.00	0.00	T9		6,410.00	-		
					6410.00 to PI 8	23/07/2016	O/Bal					6,410.00			
58	BP	1200				15/07/2016	DD	132.40	0.00		Y	132.40		R	31/07/2016
		58	7103	0	Granby Council business			132.40	0.00	T2		132.40	N		
59	CP	1230				05/07/2016	054	10.17	2.03		Y	12.20			-
		59	7801	0	Cleaning materials			10.17	2.03	T1		12.20	N		
60	CP	1230				06/07/2016	055	15.00	0.00		Y	15.00			
		60	8200	0	Donation to local charity			15.00	0.00	T9		15.00	-		
61	CP	1230				10/07/2016	056	14.80	0.00		Y	14.80			
		61	7400	0	Train ticket to event			14.80	0.00	T2		14.80	N		
62	CP	1230				10/07/2016	057	5.20	1.04		Y	6.24			
		62	7502	0	Printer paper			5.20	1.04	T1		6.24	N		
63	JC	1200				11/07/2016	024225	48.24	0.00		Y	48.24		R	31/07/2016
		63	1200	0	Restore petty cash			48.24	0.00	T9		48.24	-		
64	JD	1230				11/07/2016	024225	48.24	0.00		Y	48.24			
		64	1230	0	Restore petty cash			48.24	0.00	T9		48.24	-		
65	JD	0030				30/07/2016	012	3,748.00	0.00		Y	3,748.00			
		65	0030	0	Correction of error			3,748.00	0.00	T9		3,748.00	-		
66	JC	0040				30/07/2016	012	3,748.00	0.00		Y	3,748.00			
		66	0040	0	Correction of error			3,748.00	0.00	T9		3,748.00	-		
67	BP	1200				30/07/2016		22.00	0.00		Y	22.00		R	31/07/2016
		67	7901	0	Bank charges			22.00	0.00	T2		22.00	N		
68	SR	AGC01				05/07/2016	BACS	856.80	0.00		Y	856.80		R	31/07/2016
		68	1200	0	Sales Receipt			856.80	0.00	T9		856.80	-		
					76.80 to SI 25	05/07/2016	00895					76.80			
					60.00 to SI 26	05/07/2016	00895					60.00			
					720.00 to SI 27	05/07/2016	00895					720.00			

Evidence 4 – Trial balance as at 31 July 20-X

| Date: | | **Clifton Card Warehouse** | | **Page:** 1 |
| Time: | | **Period Trial Balance** | | |

To Period: Month 1, July 2016

N/C	Name	Debit	Credit
0030	Office Equipment	3,748.00	
0040	Furniture and Fixtures	32,018.67	
0041	Furniture/Fixture Depreciation		5,197.50
1100	Debtors Control Account	2,854.50	
1200	Bank Current Account	12,004.91	
1210	Bank Deposit Account	6,000.00	
1230	Petty Cash	50.00	
2100	Creditors Control Account		11,274.05
2200	Sales Tax Control Account		11,718.25
2201	Purchase Tax Control Account	3,821.44	
3000	Capital		27,591.23
4000	Sales - Greetings cards		3,738.00
4001	Sales - Gift wrap		64.00
4002	Sales - Decorations		1,108.00
4003	Sales - Online sales		9,781.25
5000	Purchases (Gift cards)	3,772.29	
5001	Purchases (Decorations/Gift wrap)	5,360.90	
6201	Advertising	642.00	
7103	General Rates	132.40	
7400	Travelling	14.80	
7502	Office Stationery	5.20	
7801	Cleaning	10.17	
7901	Bank Charges	22.00	
8200	Donations	15.00	
	Totals:	70,472.28	70,472.28

Evidence 5a – Screenshot of the recurring entry set up screen, including all relevant input detail

© 2016 Sage (UK) Limited. All rights reserved.

Evidence 5b – Screenshot of the amended recurring entry set up screen, including all relevant input detail.

© 2016 Sage (UK) Limited. All rights reserved.

Evidence 6 – Screenshot of the bank reconciliation screen showing reconciled items

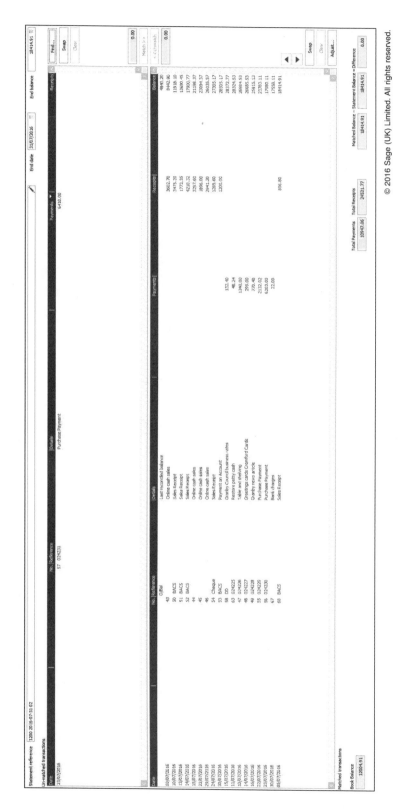

or

Date:
Time:

Clifton Card Warehouse
Bank Reconciled Transactions

Page: 1

Bank Reconciled On: 01/07/2016

No	Type	Date	A/C	N/C	Dept	Ref	Details	Net	Tax	T/C
9	JD	01/07/2016	1200	1200	0	O/Bal	Opening Balance	4,840.20	0.00	T9

Bank Reconciled On: 31/07/2016

No	Type	Date	A/C	N/C	Dept	Ref	Details	Net	Tax	T/C
43	BR	08/07/2016	1200	4003	0		Online cash sales	3,002.25	600.45	T1
44	BR	15/07/2016	1200	4003	0		Online cash sales	2,748.00	549.60	T1
45	BR	22/07/2016	1200	4003	0		Online cash sales	1,580.00	316.00	T1
46	BR	29/07/2016	1200	4003	0		Online cash sales	2,451.00	490.20	T1
47	BP	10/07/2016	1200	0040	0	024226	Table and shelving	1,116.67	223.33	T1
48	BP	14/07/2016	1200	5000	0	024227	Greetings cards Cromford	249.17	49.83	T1
49	BP	16/07/2016	1200	6201	0	024228	Granby news article	642.00	128.40	T1
50	SR	10/07/2016	MP01	1200	0	BACS	Sales Receipt	3,475.20	0.00	T9
51	SR	13/07/2016	CC01	1200	0	BACS	Sales Receipt	1,772.35	0.00	T9
52	SR	14/07/2016	AGC01	1200	0	BACS	Sales Receipt	4,210.32	0.00	T9
53	SA	30/07/2016	AGC01	1200	0	BACS	Payment on Account	1,200.00	0.00	T9
54	SR	24/07/2016	BGC01	1200	0	Cheque	Sales Receipt	1,269.60	0.00	T9
55	PP	22/07/2016	SCS01	1200	0	024229	Purchase Payment	2,132.02	0.00	T9
56	PP	23/07/2016	BW01	1200	0	024230	Purchase Payment	6,203.00	0.00	T9
58	BP	15/07/2016	1200	7103	0	DD	Granby Council business	132.40	0.00	T2
63	JC	11/07/2016	1200	1200	0	024225	Restore petty cash	48.24	0.00	T9
67	BP	30/07/2016	1200	7901	0		Bank charges	22.00	0.00	T2
68	SR	05/07/2016	AGC01	1200	0	BACS	Sales Receipt	856.80	0.00	T9

Answers to practice assessment 4

Task	Transaction Type	Account(s)		Date 20-X	Net Amount £	VAT £	Allocated against receipt/ payment ✓	Reconciled with bank statement ✓
1	Customer O/bal	FC01		1 Aug	6,542.20		✓	
	Customer O/bal	FSS02		1 Aug	3,339.90		✓	
	Customer O/bal	NLC01		1 Aug	2,010.20		✓	
	Customer O/bal	NC02		1 Aug	7,542.00		✓	
2	Supplier O/bal	ROS01		1 Aug	4,350.00		✓	
	Supplier O/bal	SS01		1 Aug	2,230.00		✓	
	Supplier O/bal	TKAS01		1 Aug	3,740.60		✓	
	Supplier O/bal	WSL01		1 Aug	1,635.55			
3	Cr	Bank current account		1 Aug	2,403.00			✓
	Dr	Petty cash		1 Aug	100.00			
	Dr	Motor vehicles - cost		1 Aug	8,730.50			
	Cr	Motor vehicles – accumulated depreciation		1 Aug	1,746.10			
	Dr	Office equipment - cost		1 Aug	12,707.70			
	Cr	Office equipment - accumulated depreciation		1 Aug	1,524.92			
	Dr	Sales ledger control *		1 Aug	19,434.30			
	Cr	Purchase ledger control *		1 Aug	11,956.15			
	Cr	VAT on sales		1 Aug	6,502.40			
	Dr	VAT on purchases		1 Aug	1,870.46			
	Cr	Capital		1 Aug	18,710.39			
		*If appropriate						
4	Sales inv	NC02	Sales:	2 Aug				
			Filing and folders		375.00	75.00	✓	
			Paper		1,274.00	254.80	✓	
			Filing and folders		2,100.00	420.00	✓	
	Sales CN	FC01	Sales:	6 Aug				
			Ink		174.00	34.80	✓	
			Filing and folders		21.00	4.20	✓	
	Sales inv	FSS02	Sales:	14 Aug				
			Paper		59.80	11.96		
			Paper		59.80	11.96		
			Filing and folders		210.00	42.00		
			Ink		2,230.00	446.00		
	Sales CN	NC02	Sales:	16 Aug				
			Filing and folders		17.50	3.50	✓	
			Paper		45.50	9.10	✓	
5	Purchase inv	TKAS01	Office equipment	8 Aug	1,161.20	232.24	✓	
	Purchase inv	WSL01	Repairs and renewals	9 Aug	6.90	1.38		
			Advertising		351.96	70.39		
	Purchase inv	SS01	Purchases	11 Aug	15,740.30	3,148.06	✓	
	Purchase CN	SS01	Purchases	15 Aug	3,541.20	708.24	✓	
6	Bank receipt	Bank	Sales Online	5 Aug	6,595.20			✓
	Bank receipt	Bank	Sales Online	12 Aug	5,009.16			✓
	Bank receipt	Bank	Sales Online	19 Aug	4,802.40			✓
	Bank receipt	Bank	Sales Online	26 Aug	3,528.00			✓
	Bank payment	Bank	Recruitment	14 Aug	575.00	115.00		✓
	Bank payment	Bank	Telephone	30 Aug	65.00	13.00		
	Bank receipt	Bank	Sales – Filing and folders	18 Aug	331.67	66.33		
	Bank receipt	Bank	Loan	13 Aug	20,000.00			✓
	Dr	Deposit		27 Aug	15,000.00			✓
	Cr	Bank Current		27 Aug	15,000.00			✓

7	Customer receipt	NC02	Bank	20 Aug	11,905.20			✓	✓
	Customer receipt	NLC01	Bank	21 Aug	2,010.20			✓	✓
	Customer receipt	FC01	Bank	12 Aug	6,308.20			✓	✓
	Customer receipt	FSS02	Bank	12 Aug	3,339.90			✓	✓
	Customer receipt	FSS02	Bank	18 Aug	2,400.00				✓
8	Supplier payment	ROS01	Bank	22 Aug	4,350.00			✓	✓
	Supplier payment	SS01	Bank	22 Aug	16,868.92				✓
	Supplier payment	WSL01	Bank	22 Aug	5,000.00				✓
	Supplier payment	TKAS01	Bank	14 Aug	5,134.04			✓	✓
9	Bank payment	Bank	Office equipment maintenance – DD	24 Aug	72.60	14.52			✓
	Bank receipt	Bank	Rental Income	25 Aug	320.00	64.00			✓
10	Dr	Petty cash		2 Aug	50.00				
	Cr	Bank		2 Aug	50.00				✓
	Cash payment	Petty cash	Postage	2 Aug	6.36				
	Cash payment	Petty cash	Miscellaneous expenses	5 Aug	22.10	4.42			
	Cash payment	Petty cash	Miscellaneous expenses	8 Aug	6.92	1.38			
11	Journal debit	Sales - Ink		12 Aug	64.80				
	Journal credit	Sales – Filing and folders		12 Aug	64.80				
11	Journal debit	Drawings		20 Aug	350.00				
	Journal credit	Materials purchased		20 Aug	350.00				
12	Bank payment	Bank	Bank charges	30 Aug	40.00				✓

Evidence 1a – All customer transactions

<table>
<tr><td>**Date:**</td><td colspan="4" align="center">**Southglade Stationery Warehouse**</td><td>**Page:** 1</td></tr>
<tr><td>**Time:**</td><td colspan="4" align="center">**Customer Activity (Detailed)**</td><td></td></tr>
</table>

Date From:	01/01/1980	**Customer From:**
Date To:	31/08/2016	**Customer To:** ZZZZZZZZ
Transaction From:	1	**N/C From:**
Transaction To:	99,999,999	**N/C To:** 99999999
Inc b/fwd transaction:	No	**Dept From:** 0
Exc later payment:	No	**Dept To:** 999

** NOTE: All report values are shown in Base Currency, unless otherwise indicated **

A/C: FC01   **Name:** Farnsworth College   **Contact:** David Roberts   **Tel:** 0198 332113

No	Type	Date	Ref	N/C	Details	Dept	T/C	Value	O/S	Debit	Credit	V	B
1	SI	01/08/2016	O/Bal	9998	Opening Balance	0	T9	6,542.20		6,542.20		-	-
30	SC	06/08/2016	047	4000	Faulty ink cartridges	0	T1	208.80			208.80	N	-
31	SC	06/08/2016	047	4002	Damaged folders	0	T1	25.20			25.20	N	-
55	SR	12/08/2016	BACS	1200	Sales Receipt	0	T9	6,308.20			6,308.20	-	R
							Totals:		0.00	0.00	6,542.20	6,542.20	

Amount Outstanding	0.00
Amount Paid this period	6,308.20
Credit Limit £	9,000.00
Turnover YTD	6,347.20

A/C: FSS02   **Name:** Fusion Stationery Supplies   **Contact:** Janet Spencer   **Tel:** 0150 963424

No	Type	Date	Ref	N/C	Details	Dept	T/C	Value	O/S	Debit	Credit	V	B
2	SI	01/08/2016	O/Bal	9998	Opening Balance	0	T9	3,339.90		3,339.90		-	-
32	SI	14/08/2016	007141	4001	Blue paper	0	T1	71.76 *	71.76	71.76		N	-
33	SI	14/08/2016	007141	4001	Green paper	0	T1	71.76 *	71.76	71.76		N	-
34	SI	14/08/2016	007141	4002	Document wallets	0	T1	252.00 *	252.00	252.00		N	-
35	SI	14/08/2016	007141	4000	Ink cartridges	0	T1	2,676.00 *	2,676.00	2,676.00		N	-
56	SR	12/08/2016	BACS	1200	Sales Receipt	0	T9	3,339.90			3,339.90	-	R
57	SA	18/08/2016	BACS	1200	Payment on Account	0	T9	2,400.00 *	-2,400.00		2,400.00	-	R
							Totals:		671.52	671.52	6,411.42	5,739.90	

Amount Outstanding	671.52
Amount Paid this period	5,739.90
Credit Limit £	22,000.00
Turnover YTD	5,899.50

A/C: NC02   **Name:** Northgate College   **Contact:** Lukasz Cservenyak   **Tel:** 0150 077360

No	Type	Date	Ref	N/C	Details	Dept	T/C	Value	O/S	Debit	Credit	V	B
4	SI	01/08/2016	O/Bal	9998	Opening Balance	0	T9	7,542.00		7,542.00		-	-
27	SI	02/08/2016	007140	4002	A5 folders	0	T1	450.00		450.00		N	-
28	SI	02/08/2016	007140	4001	A4 paper	0	T1	1,528.80		1,528.80		N	-
29	SI	02/08/2016	007140	4002	Lever arch files	0	T1	2,520.00		2,520.00		N	-
36	SC	16/08/2016	048	4002	Folders returned	0	T1	21.00			21.00	N	-
37	SC	16/08/2016	048	4001	Copier paper returned	0	T1	54.60			54.60	N	-
53	SR	20/08/2016	Cheque	1200	Sales Receipt	0	T9	11,965.20			11,965.20	-	R
							Totals:		0.00	0.00	12,040.80	12,040.80	

Amount Outstanding	0.00
Amount Paid this period	11,965.20
Credit Limit £	12,100.00
Turnover YTD	11,228.00

A/C: NLC01   **Name:** Newbridge Learning Centre   **Contact:** Samuel Impellizzeri   **Tel:** 0198 213452

No	Type	Date	Ref	N/C	Details	Dept	T/C	Value	O/S	Debit	Credit	V	B
3	SI	01/08/2016	O/Bal	9998	Opening Balance	0	T9	2,010.20		2,010.20		-	-
54	SR	21/08/2016	Cheque	1200	Sales Receipt	0	T9	2,010.20			2,010.20	-	R
							Totals:		0.00	0.00	2,010.20	2,010.20	

Amount Outstanding	0.00
Amount Paid this period	2,010.20
Credit Limit £	8,250.00
Turnover YTD	2,010.20

Evidence 1b – Balance owed by each customer

Southglade Stationery Warehouse
Aged Debtors Analysis (Summary)

Date:						Page:	1

Report Date:	31/08/2016
Include future transactions:	No
Exclude later payments:	No

Customer From:
Customer To: ZZZZZZZZ

** NOTE: All report values are shown in Base Currency, unless otherwise indicated **

A/C	Name	Credit Limit	Turnover	Balance	Future	Current	Period 1	Period 2	Period 3	Older
FSS02	Fusion Stationery Supplies	£ 22,000.00	5,899.50	671.52	0.00	671.52	0.00	0.00	0.00	0.00
	Totals:		5,899.50	671.52	0.00	671.52	0.00	0.00	0.00	0.00

Evidence 2 – Screen to show the payment terms (note the headings can be changed on the customer's home screen to display the payment terms).

A/C	Name	Balance	Credit Limit	Contact	Telephone	Payment Due Days
FC01	Farnsworth College	0.00	9000.00	David Roberts	0198 332113	30
FSS02	Fusion Stationery Supplies	671.52	22000.00	Janet Spencer	0159 963424	30
NC02	Northgate College	0.00	12000.00	Lukasz Ciastvenyak	0190 077360	30
NLC01	Newbridge Learning Centre	0.00	8250.00	Samuel Impelizzeri	0198 213452	30

Evidence 2a – All supplier transactions

Date:		**Southglade Stationery Warehouse**		Page:	1

Southglade Stationery Warehouse
Supplier Activity (Detailed)

Date: Page: 1
Time:

Date From:	01/01/1980	Supplier From:	
Date To:	31/08/2016	Supplier To:	ZZZZZZZZ
Transaction From:	1	N/C From:	
Transaction To:	99,999,999	N/C To:	99999999
Inc b/fwd transaction:	No	Dept From:	0
Exc later payment:	No	Dept To:	999

** NOTE: All report values are shown in Base Currency, unless otherwise indicated **

A/C: ROS01   **Name:** Riverside Office Supplies   **Contact:** Catherine Hemmingway   **Tel:** 0150 210210

No	Type	Date	Ref	N/C	Details	Dept	T/C	Value	O/S	Debit	Credit	V	B
5	PI	01/08/2016	O/Bal	9998	Opening Balance	0	T9	4,350.00	0.00		4,350.00	-	-
58	PP	22/08/2016	BACS	1200	Purchase Payment	0	T9	4,350.00	0.00	4,350.00		-	R
					Totals:			0.00	0.00	4,350.00	4,350.00		

Amount Outstanding	0.00
Amount paid this period	4,350.00
Credit Limit £	6,400.00
Turnover YTD	4,350.00

A/C: SS01   **Name:** Shelford Stationery   **Contact:** Louise Richards   **Tel:** 0197 113679

No	Type	Date	Ref	N/C	Details	Dept	T/C	Value	O/S	Debit	Credit	V	B
6	PI	01/08/2016	O/Bal	9998	Opening Balance	0	T9	2,230.00	0.00		2,230.00	-	-
41	PI	11/08/2016	012012	5000	Goods for resale	0	T1	18,888.36	0.00		18,888.36	-	-
42	PC	15/08/2016	124	5000	Damaged goods returned	0	T1	4,249.44	0.00	4,249.44		N	-
59	PP	22/08/2016	BACS	1200	Purchase Payment	0	T9	16,868.92	0.00	16,868.92		-	R
					Totals:			0.00	0.00	21,118.36	21,118.36		

Amount Outstanding	0.00
Amount paid this period	16,868.92
Credit Limit £	22,000.00
Turnover YTD	14,429.10

A/C: TKAS01   **Name:** TKA Supplies   **Contact:** Tamara Tomlinson   **Tel:** 0121 669774

No	Type	Date	Ref	N/C	Details	Dept	T/C	Value	O/S	Debit	Credit	V	B
7	PI	01/08/2016	O/Bal	9998	Opening Balance	0	T9	3,740.60	0.00		3,740.60	-	-
38	PI	08/08/2016	INV635	0030	Computers	0	T1	1,393.44	0.00		1,393.44	N	-
61	PP	14/08/2016	201635	1200	Purchase Payment	0	T9	5,134.04	0.00	5,134.04		-	R
					Totals:			0.00	0.00	5,134.04	5,134.04		

Amount Outstanding	0.00
Amount paid this period	5,134.04
Credit Limit £	5,500.00
Turnover YTD	4,901.80

A/C: WSL01   **Name:** Wilford & Son Ltd   **Contact:** Ron Wilford   **Tel:** 0150 200300

No	Type	Date	Ref	N/C	Details	Dept	T/C	Value	O/S	Debit	Credit	V	B
8	PI	01/08/2016	O/Bal	9998	Opening Balance	0	T9	1,635.55 *	1,635.55		1,635.55	-	-
39	PI	09/08/2016	6310	7800	Filing cabinet locks	0	T1	8.28 *	8.28		8.28	N	-
40	PI	09/08/2016	6310	6201	Promotional stands	0	T1	422.35 *	422.35		422.35	N	-
60	PA	22/08/2016	BACS	1200	Payment on Account	0	T9	5,000.00 *	-5,000.00	5,000.00		-	R
					Totals:			-2,933.82	-2,933.82	5,000.00	2,066.18		

Amount Outstanding	-2,933.82
Amount paid this period	5,000.00
Credit Limit £	4,200.00
Turnover YTD	1,994.41

Evidence 2b – Balance owed by suppliers

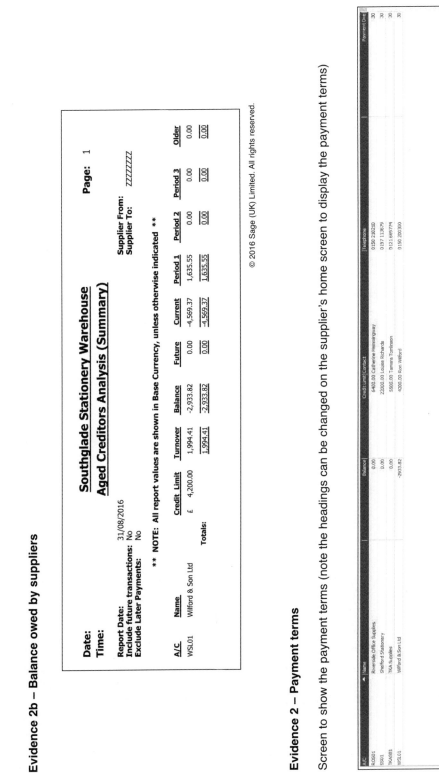

Date:
Time:

Southglade Stationery Warehouse
Aged Creditors Analysis (Summary)

Page: 1

Report Date: 31/08/2016
Include future transactions: No
Exclude Later Payments: No

Supplier From:
Supplier To: ZZZZZZZZ

** NOTE: All report values are shown in Base Currency, unless otherwise indicated **

A/C	Name	Credit Limit	Turnover	Balance	Future	Current	Period 1	Period 2	Period 3	Older
WSL01	Wilford & Son Ltd	£ 4,200.00	1,994.41	-2,933.82	0.00	-4,569.37	1,635.55	0.00	0.00	0.00
	Totals:		1,994.41	-2,933.82	0.00	-4,569.37	1,635.55	0.00	0.00	0.00

Evidence 2 – Payment terms

Screen to show the payment terms (note the headings can be changed on the supplier's home screen to display the payment terms)

A/C	Name	Balance	Credit Limit	Contact	Telephone	Payment Due
ROS01	Riverside Office Supplies	0.00	6400.00	Catherine Hemmingway	0150 230210	30
SS01	Shelford Stationery	0.00	22000.00	Louise Richards	0197 113679	30
TKA001	TKA Supplies	0.00	5900.00	Tamara Tomlinson	0121 669774	30
WSL01	Wilford & Son Ltd	-2933.82	4200.00	Ron Wilford	0150 200300	30

Evidence 2c – Remittance advice for Riverside Office Supplies

Southglade Stationery Warehouse
Unit 3
810 Southglade Road
Newbridge
NE6 6RB

Tel :

VAT Reg No.

Riverside Office Supplies
52 Riverside Way

Filey

FG1 2NP

REMITTANCE ADVICE

Date	22/08/2016
Account Ref	ROS01
Cheque No	BACS

NOTE: All values are shown in Pound Sterling

Date	Ref	Details	Debit	Credit
01/08/2016	O/Bal	Opening Balance		4,350.00

	Amount Paid
£	4,350.00

Evidence 3 – An audit trail, showing full details of all transactions, including details of receipts/payments allocated to items in customer/supplier accounts and details of items in the bank account that have been reconciled.

Date:					Southglade Stationery Warehouse									Page: 1
Time:					Audit Trail (Detailed)									

Date From:	01/01/1980			Customer From:	
Date To:	31/12/2019			Customer To:	ZZZZZZZZ
Transaction From:	1			Supplier From:	
Transaction To:	99,999,999			Supplier To:	ZZZZZZZZ

Exclude Deleted Tran: No

No	Type	A/C	N/C	Dept	Details	Date	Ref	Net	Tax	T/C	Pd	Paid	V	B	Bank Rec.
1	SI	FC01				01/08/2016	O/Bal	6,542.20	0.00		Y	6,542.20	-		
		1	9998	0	Opening Balance			6,542.20	0.00	T9		6,542.20	-		
					208.80 from SC 30	06/08/2016	047					208.80			
					25.20 from SC 31	06/08/2016	047					25.20			
					6308.20 from SR 55	12/08/2016	BACS					6,308.20			
2	SI	FSS02				01/08/2016	O/Bal	3,339.90	0.00		Y	3,339.90	-		
		2	9998	0	Opening Balance			3,339.90	0.00	T9		3,339.90	-		
					3339.90 from SR 56	12/08/2016	BACS					3,339.90			
3	SI	NLC01				01/08/2016	O/Bal	2,010.20	0.00		Y	2,010.20	-		
		3	9998	0	Opening Balance			2,010.20	0.00	T9		2,010.20	-		
					2010.20 from SR 54	21/08/2016	Cheque					2,010.20			
4	SI	NC02				01/08/2016	O/Bal	7,542.00	0.00		Y	7,542.00	-		
		4	9998	0	Opening Balance			7,542.00	0.00	T9		7,542.00	-		
					21.00 from SC 36	16/08/2016	048					21.00			
					54.60 from SC 37	16/08/2016	048					54.60			
					7466.40 from SR 53	20/08/2016	Cheque					7,466.40			
5	PI	ROS01				01/08/2016	O/Bal	4,350.00	0.00		Y	4,350.00	-		
		5	9998	0	Opening Balance			4,350.00	0.00	T9		4,350.00	-		
					4350.00 from PP 58	22/08/2016	BACS					4,350.00			
6	PI	SS01				01/08/2016	O/Bal	2,230.00	0.00		Y	2,230.00	-		
		6	9998	0	Opening Balance			2,230.00	0.00	T9		2,230.00	-		
					2230.00 from PC 42	15/08/2016	124					2,230.00			
7	PI	TKAS01				01/08/2016	O/Bal	3,740.60	0.00		Y	3,740.60	-		
		7	9998	0	Opening Balance			3,740.60	0.00	T9		3,740.60	-		
					3740.60 from PP 61	14/08/2016	201635					3,740.60			
8	PI	WSL01				01/08/2016	O/Bal	1,635.55	0.00		N	0.00	-		
		8	9998	0	Opening Balance			1,635.55	0.00	T9		0.00	-		
9	JC	1200				01/08/2016	O/Bal	2,403.00	0.00		Y	2,403.00	-		01/08/2016
		9	1200	0	Opening Balance			2,403.00	0.00	T9		2,403.00	-		

Date: Time:					Southglade Stationery Warehouse Audit Trail (Detailed)								Page: 2		
No	**Type**	**A/C**	**N/C**	**Dept**	**Details**	**Date**	**Ref**	**Net**	**Tax**	**T/C**	**Pd**	**Paid**	**V**	**B**	**Bank Rec.**
10	JD	9998				01/08/2016	O/Bal	2,403.00	0.00		Y	2,403.00	-		
		10	9998	0	Opening Balance			2,403.00	0.00	T9		2,403.00 -			
11	JD	1230				01/08/2016	O/Bal	100.00	0.00		Y	100.00	-		01/08/2016
		11	1230	0	Opening Balance			100.00	0.00	T9		100.00 -			
12	JC	9998				01/08/2016	O/Bal	100.00	0.00		Y	100.00	-		
		12	9998	0	Opening Balance			100.00	0.00	T9		100.00 -			
13	JD	0050				01/08/2016	O/Bal	8,730.50	0.00		Y	8,730.50	-		
		13	0050	0	Opening Balance			8,730.50	0.00	T9		8,730.50 -			
14	JC	9998				01/08/2016	O/Bal	8,730.50	0.00		Y	8,730.50	-		
		14	9998	0	Opening Balance			8,730.50	0.00	T9		8,730.50 -			
15	JC	0051				01/08/2016	O/Bal	1,746.10	0.00		Y	1,746.10	-		
		15	0051	0	Opening Balance			1,746.10	0.00	T9		1,746.10 -			
16	JD	9998				01/08/2016	O/Bal	1,746.10	0.00		Y	1,746.10	-		
		16	9998	0	Opening Balance			1,746.10	0.00	T9		1,746.10 -			
17	JD	0030				01/08/2016	O/Bal	12,707.70	0.00		Y	12,707.70	-		
		17	0030	0	Opening Balance			12,707.70	0.00	T9		12,707.70 -			
18	JC	9998				01/08/2016	O/Bal	12,707.70	0.00		Y	12,707.70	-		
		18	9998	0	Opening Balance			12,707.70	0.00	T9		12,707.70 -			
19	JC	0031				01/08/2016	O/Bal	1,524.92	0.00		Y	1,524.92	-		
		19	0031	0	Opening Balance			1,524.92	0.00	T9		1,524.92 -			
20	JD	9998				01/08/2016	O/Bal	1,524.92	0.00		Y	1,524.92	-		
		20	9998	0	Opening Balance			1,524.92	0.00	T9		1,524.92 -			
21	JC	2200				01/08/2016	O/Bal	6,502.40	0.00		Y	6,502.40	-		
		21	2200	0	Opening Balance			6,502.40	0.00	T9		6,502.40 -			
22	JD	9998				01/08/2016	O/Bal	6,502.40	0.00		Y	6,502.40	-		
		22	9998	0	Opening Balance			6,502.40	0.00	T9		6,502.40 -			
23	JD	2201				01/08/2016	O/Bal	1,870.46	0.00		Y	1,870.46	-		
		23	2201	0	Opening Balance			1,870.46	0.00	T9		1,870.46 -			
24	JC	9998				01/08/2016	O/Bal	1,870.46	0.00		Y	1,870.46	-		
		24	9998	0	Opening Balance			1,870.46	0.00	T9		1,870.46 -			
25	JC	3000				01/08/2016	O/Bal	18,710.39	0.00		Y	18,710.39	-		
		25	3000	0	Opening Balance			18,710.39	0.00	T9		18,710.39 -			
26	JD	9998				01/08/2016	O/Bal	18,710.39	0.00		Y	18,710.39	-		
		26	9998	0	Opening Balance			18,710.39	0.00	T9		18,710.39 -			
27	SI	NC02				02/08/2016	007140	3,749.00	749.80		Y	4,498.80	-		
		27	4002	0	A5 folders			375.00	75.00	T1		450.00	N		
					450.00 from SR 53	20/08/2016	Cheque					450.00			
		28	4001	0	A4 paper			1,274.00	254.80	T1		1,528.80	N		
					1528.80 from SR 53	20/08/2016	Cheque					1,528.80			
		29	4002	0	Lever arch files			2,100.00	420.00	T1		2,520.00	N		
					2520.00 from SR 53	20/08/2016	Cheque					2,520.00			
30	SC	FC01				06/08/2016	047	195.00	39.00		Y	234.00	-		
		30	4000	0	Faulty ink cartridges			174.00	34.80	T1		208.80	N		
					208.80 to SI 1	06/08/2016	O/Bal					208.80			
		31	4002	0	Damaged folders			21.00	4.20	T1		25.20	N		
					25.20 to SI 1	06/08/2016	O/Bal					25.20			
32	SI	FSS02				14/08/2016	007141	2,559.60	511.92		N	0.00	-		
		32	4001	0	Blue paper			59.80	11.96	T1		0.00	N		
		33	4001	0	Green paper			59.80	11.96	T1		0.00	N		
		34	4002	0	Document wallets			210.00	42.00	T1		0.00	N		
		35	4000	0	Ink cartridges			2,230.00	446.00	T1		0.00	N		
36	SC	NC02				16/08/2016	048	63.00	12.60		Y	75.60	-		
		36	4002	0	Folders returned			17.50	3.50	T1		21.00	N		
					21.00 to SI 4	16/08/2016	O/Bal					21.00			
		37	4001	0	Copier paper returned			45.50	9.10	T1		54.60	N		
					54.60 to SI 4	16/08/2016	O/Bal					54.60			
38	PI	TKAS01				08/08/2016	INV635	1,161.20	232.24		Y	1,393.44	-		
		38	0030	0	Computers			1,161.20	232.24	T1		1,393.44	N		
					1393.44 from PP 61	14/08/2016	201635					1,393.44			
39	PI	WSL01				09/08/2016	6310	358.86	71.77		N	0.00	-		
		39	7800	0	Filing cabinet locks			6.90	1.38	T1		0.00	N		
		40	6201	0	Promotional stands			351.96	70.39	T1		0.00	N		
41	PI	SS01				11/08/2016	012012	15,740.30	3,148.06		Y	18,888.36	-		
		41	5000	0	Goods for resale			15,740.30	3,148.06	T1		18,888.36	N		
					2019.44 from PC 42	15/08/2016	124					2,019.44			
					16868.92 from PP 59	22/08/2016	BACS					16,868.92			
42	PC	SS01				15/08/2016	124	3,541.20	708.24		Y	4,249.44	-		
		42	5000	0	Damaged goods returned			3,541.20	708.24	T1		4,249.44	N		
					2230.00 to PI 6	15/08/2016	O/Bal					2,230.00			
					2019.44 to PI 41	15/08/2016	012012					2,019.44			
43	BR	1200				05/08/2016		5,496.00	1,099.20		Y	6,595.20		R	31/08/2016

Date: Time:					**Southglade Stationery Warehouse** **Audit Trail (Detailed)**							Page: 4			
No	**Type**	**A/C**	**N/C**	**Dept**	**Details**	**Date**	**Ref**	**Net**	**Tax**	**T/C**	**Pd**	**Paid**	**V**	**B**	**Bank Rec.**
		43	4003	0	Online cash sales			5,496.00	1,099.20	T1		6,595.20	N		
44	BR	1200				12/08/2016		4,174.30	834.86		Y	5,009.16		R	31/08/2016
		44	4003	0	Online cash sales			4,174.30	834.86	T1		5,009.16	N		
45	BR	1200				19/08/2016		4,002.00	800.40		Y	4,802.40		R	31/08/2016
		45	4003	0	Online cash sales			4,002.00	800.40	T1		4,802.40	N		
46	BR	1200				26/08/2016		2,940.00	588.00		Y	3,528.00		R	31/08/2016
		46	4003	0	Online cash sales			2,940.00	588.00	T1		3,528.00	N		
47	BP	1200				14/08/2016	201634	575.00	115.00		Y	690.00		R	31/08/2016
		47	6201	0	Southglade advert			575.00	115.00	T1		690.00	N		
48	BP	1200				30/08/2016	201636	65.00	13.00		Y	78.00		N	
		48	7550	0	Thorpe telephones			65.00	13.00	T1		78.00	N		
49	BR	1200				18/08/2016	94	331.67	66.33		Y	398.00		R	31/08/2016
		49	4002	0	Folders			331.67	66.33	T1		398.00	N		
50	BR	1200				13/08/2016	Receipt	20,000.00	0.00		Y	20,000.00		R	31/08/2016
		50	2300	0	Bank loan received			20,000.00	0.00	T9		20,000.00	-		
51	JC	1200				27/08/2016	TRANS	15,000.00	0.00		Y	15,000.00		R	31/08/2016
		51	1200	0	Bank Transfer			15,000.00	0.00	T9		15,000.00	-		
52	JD	1210				27/08/2016	TRANS	15,000.00	0.00		Y	15,000.00		N	
		52	1210	0	Bank Transfer			15,000.00	0.00	T9		15,000.00	-		
53	SR	NC02				20/08/2016	Cheque	11,965.20	0.00		Y	11,965.20		R	31/08/2016
		53	1200	0	Sales Receipt			11,965.20	0.00	T9		11,965.20	-		
					7466.40 to SI 4	20/08/2016	O/Bal					7,466.40			
					450.00 to SI 27	20/08/2016	007140					450.00			
					1528.80 to SI 28	20/08/2016	007140					1,528.80			
					2520.00 to SI 29	20/08/2016	007140					2,520.00			
54	SR	NLC01				21/08/2016	Cheque	2,010.20	0.00		Y	2,010.20		R	31/08/2016
		54	1200	0	Sales Receipt			2,010.20	0.00	T9		2,010.20	-		
					2010.20 to SI 3	21/08/2016	O/Bal					2,010.20			
55	SR	FC01				12/08/2016	BACS	6,308.20	0.00		Y	6,308.20		R	31/08/2016
		55	1200	0	Sales Receipt			6,308.20	0.00	T9		6,308.20	-		
					6308.20 to SI 1	12/08/2016	O/Bal					6,308.20			
56	SR	FSS02				12/08/2016	BACS	3,339.90	0.00		Y	3,339.90		R	31/08/2016
		56	1200	0	Sales Receipt			3,339.90	0.00	T9		3,339.90	-		
					3339.90 to SI 2	12/08/2016	O/Bal					3,339.90			
57	SA	FSS02				18/08/2016	BACS	2,400.00	0.00		N	0.00		R	31/08/2016
		57	1200	0	Payment on Account			2,400.00	0.00	T9		0.00	-		
58	PP	ROS01				22/08/2016	BACS	4,350.00	0.00		Y	4,350.00		R	31/08/2016
		58	1200	0	Purchase Payment			4,350.00	0.00	T9		4,350.00	-		
					4350.00 to PI 5	22/08/2016	O/Bal					4,350.00			
59	PP	SS01				22/08/2016	BACS	16,868.92	0.00		Y	16,868.92		R	31/08/2016
		59	1200	0	Purchase Payment			16,868.92	0.00	T9		16,868.92	-		
					16868.92 to PI 41	22/08/2016	012012					16,868.92			
60	PA	WSL01				22/08/2016	BACS	5,000.00	0.00		N	0.00		R	31/08/2016
		60	1200	0	Payment on Account			5,000.00	0.00	T9		0.00	-		
61	PP	TKAS01				14/08/2016	201635	5,134.04	0.00		Y	5,134.04		R	31/08/2016
		61	1200	0	Purchase Payment			5,134.04	0.00	T9		5,134.04	-		
					3740.60 to PI 7	14/08/2016	O/Bal					3,740.60			
					1393.44 to PI 38	14/08/2016	INV635					1,393.44			
62	BR	1200				25/08/2016	STO	320.00	64.00		Y	384.00		R	31/08/2016
		62	4904	0	Rental income from Harris			320.00	64.00	T1		384.00	N		
63	BP	1200				28/08/2016	DD	72.60	14.52		Y	87.12		R	31/08/2016
		63	7701	0	PH Photocopiers			72.60	14.52	T1		87.12	N		
64	JC	1200				02/08/2016	201633	50.00	0.00		Y	50.00		R	31/08/2016
		64	1200	0	Restore petty cash			50.00	0.00	T9		50.00	-		
65	JD	1230				02/08/2016	201633	50.00	0.00		Y	50.00			
		65	1230	0	Restore petty cash			50.00	0.00	T9		50.00	-		
66	CP	1230				02/08/2016	PC301	6.36	0.00		Y	6.36			
		66	7501	0	Stamps			6.36	0.00	T2		6.36	N		
67	CP	1230				05/08/2016	PC302	22.10	4.42		Y	26.52			
		67	6900	0	Cups for water machine			22.10	4.42	T1		26.52	N		
68	CP	1230				08/08/2016	PC303	6.92	1.38		Y	8.30			
		68	6900	0	Plants for reception			6.92	1.38	T1		8.30	N		
69	JD	4000				12/08/2016	017	64.80	0.00		Y	64.80			
		69	4000	0	Correction of error			64.80	0.00	T9		64.80	-		
70	JC	4002				12/08/2016	017	64.80	0.00		Y	64.80			
		70	4002	0	Correction of error			64.80	0.00	T9		64.80	-		
71	JD	3050				20/08/2016	018	350.00	0.00		Y	350.00			
		71	3050	0	Correction of error			350.00	0.00	T9		350.00	-		
72	JC	5000				20/08/2016	018	350.00	0.00		Y	350.00			

No	Type	A/C	N/C	Dept	Details	Date	Ref	Net	Tax	T/C	Pd	Paid	V	B	Bank Rec.
		72	5000	0	Correction of error			350.00	0.00	T9		350.00	-		
73	BP	1200				30/08/2016		40.00	0.00		Y	40.00	R		31/08/2016
		73	7901	0	Bank charges			40.00	0.00	T2		40.00	N		

Southglade Stationery Warehouse
Audit Trail (Detailed)
Page: 6

Evidence 4 – Trial balance as at 31 August 20-X

Southglade Stationery Warehouse
Period Trial Balance
Page: 1

To Period: Month 1, August 2016

N/C	Name	Debit	Credit
0030	Office Equipment	13,868.90	
0031	Office Equipment Depreciation		1,524.92
0050	Motor Vehicles	8,730.50	
0051	Motor Vehicles Depreciation		1,746.10
1100	Debtors Control Account	671.52	
1200	Bank Current Account	17,039.18	
1210	Bank Deposit Account	15,000.00	
1230	Petty Cash	108.82	
2100	Creditors Control Account	2,933.82	
2200	Sales Tax Control Account		11,165.31
2201	Purchase Tax Control Account	4,762.61	
2300	Loans		20,000.00
3000	Capital		18,710.39
3050	Drawings	350.00	
4000	Sales - Ink		1,991.20
4001	Sales - Paper		1,348.10
4002	Sales - Filing and folders		3,042.97
4003	Sales - Online sales		16,612.30
4904	Rent Income		320.00
5000	Materials Purchased	11,849.10	
6201	Advertising	926.96	
6900	Miscellaneous Expenses	29.02	
7501	Postage and Carriage	6.36	
7550	Telephone and Fax	65.00	
7701	Office Machine Maintenance	72.60	
7800	Repairs and Renewals	6.90	
7901	Bank Charges	40.00	
	Totals:	76,461.29	76,461.29

**Evidence 5a –
Screenshot of the
recurring entry set
up screen, including
all relevant input
detail**

Add / Edit Recurring Entry

Recurring Entry From / To

Bank A/C From* | 1200 | Bank Current Account
Nominal Code* | 7701 | Office Machine Maintenance

Recurring Entry Details

Transaction Type | Bank/Cash/Credit Card Payment
Transaction Ref | DD
Transaction Details | PH Photocopiers maintenance
Department* | 0 | Default

Posting Frequency

Every* | 1 | Month(s) | Total Required Postings | 10
Start Date* | 24/08/2016 | Finish Date | 24/05/2017
Next Posting Date | 24/08/2016 | Suspend Posting ? | ☐
Last Posted |

Posting Amounts

Net Amount | 72.60 | Tax Code* | T1 20.00 | VAT | 14.52

OK   Cancel

**Evidence 5b –
Screenshot of the
recurring entry set
up screen, including
all relevant input
detail**

Add / Edit Recurring Entry

Recurring Entry From / To

Bank A/C To* | 1200 | Bank Current Account
Nominal Code* | 4904 | Rent Income

Recurring Entry Details

Transaction Type | Bank/Cash/Credit Card Receipt
Transaction Ref | STO
Transaction Details | Rental income from Harris Removals
Department* | 0 | Default

Posting Frequency

Every* | 1 | Month(s) | Total Required Postings | 6
Start Date* | 25/08/2016 | Finish Date | 25/01/2017
Next Posting Date | 25/08/2016 | Suspend Posting ? | ☐
Last Posted |

Posting Amounts

Net Amount | 320.00 | Tax Code* | T1 20.00 | VAT | 64.00

OK   Cancel

Evidence 6 – Screenshot of the bank reconciliation screen showing reconciled items.

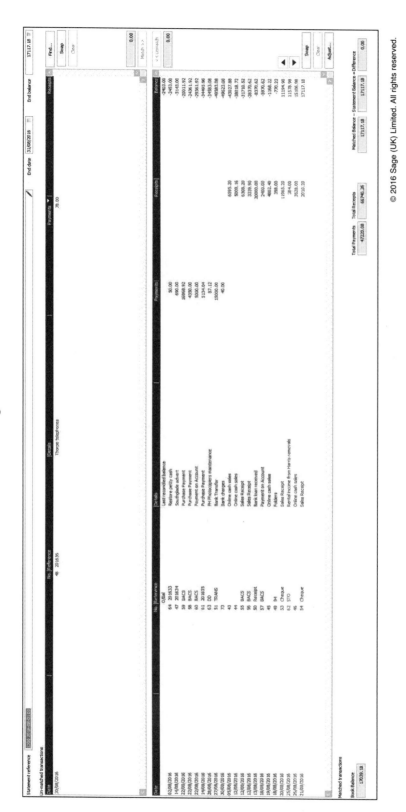

or

Date:			**Southglade Stationery Warehouse**						**Page:** 1	
Time:			**Bank Reconciled Transactions**							

Bank Reconciled On: 01/08/2016

No	Type	Date	A/C	N/C	Dept	Ref	Details	Net	Tax	T/C
9	JC	01/08/2016	1200	1200	0	O/Bal	Opening Balance	2,403.00	0.00	T9

Bank Reconciled On: 31/08/2016

No	Type	Date	A/C	N/C	Dept	Ref	Details	Net	Tax	T/C
43	BR	05/08/2016	1200	4003	0		Online cash sales	5,496.00	1,099.20	T1
44	BR	12/08/2016	1200	4003	0		Online cash sales	4,174.30	834.86	T1
45	BR	19/08/2016	1200	4003	0		Online cash sales	4,002.00	800.40	T1
46	BR	26/08/2016	1200	4003	0		Online cash sales	2,940.00	588.00	T1
47	BP	14/08/2016	1200	6201	0	201634	Southglade advert	575.00	115.00	T1
49	BR	18/08/2016	1200	4002	0	94	Folders	331.67	66.33	T1
50	BR	13/08/2016	1200	2300	0	Receipt	Bank loan received	20,000.00	0.00	T9
51	JC	27/08/2016	1200	1200	0	TRANS	Bank Transfer	15,000.00	0.00	T9
53	SR	20/08/2016	NC02	1200	0	Cheque	Sales Receipt	11,965.20	0.00	T9
54	SR	21/08/2016	NLC01	1200	0	Cheque	Sales Receipt	2,010.20	0.00	T9
55	SR	12/08/2016	FC01	1200	0	BACS	Sales Receipt	6,308.20	0.00	T9
56	SR	12/08/2016	FSS02	1200	0	BACS	Sales Receipt	3,339.90	0.00	T9
57	SA	18/08/2016	FSS02	1200	0	BACS	Payment on Account	2,400.00	0.00	T9
58	PP	22/08/2016	ROS01	1200	0	BACS	Purchase Payment	4,350.00	0.00	T9
59	PP	22/08/2016	SS01	1200	0	BACS	Purchase Payment	16,868.92	0.00	T9
60	PA	22/08/2016	WSL01	1200	0	BACS	Payment on Account	5,000.00	0.00	T9
61	PP	14/08/2016	TKAS01	1200	0	201635	Purchase Payment	5,134.04	0.00	T9
62	BR	25/08/2016	1200	4904	0	STO	Rental income from Harris	320.00	64.00	T1
63	BP	28/08/2016	1200	7701	0	DD	PH Photocopiers	72.60	14.52	T1
64	JC	02/08/2016	1200	1200	0	201633	Restore petty cash	50.00	0.00	T9
73	BP	30/08/2016	1200	7901	0		Bank charges	40.00	0.00	T2

for your notes